Gilesgate Story Chal

C000152495

Content

Once upon a time...

...in Gilesgate, a spark of an idea came to life.

Books are fun. A good story always stirs something inside of us. Children of all abilities are capable of the most fantastic creations when given time and freedom to imagine.

In a world of SATs, league tables and electronic distractions maybe people on all sides need reminding that story-telling is fun, and important.

This idea starts, as so many stories start, with a thought:

"I wonder if..."

Welcome to the first ever Gilesgate Story Challenge.

Foreword

By Simon Berry

You are about to read some fantastic stories. Our patients and the children of Durham are amazingly talented and this story competition shows the breadth of that talent and imagination.

We launched this competition on World Book Day 2019 with a very broad brief. We asked for stories that were related to eyes or vision. We didn't limit it in any other way because we wanted to keep this competition as all inclusive as possible.

I'm proud of the range of ages and abilities of the children that have been inspired enough to enter this competition. Our youngest author is 5 years old and the oldest is 16. Most of the stories have been written by individuals but some have been co-authored and represent a group effort. I am especially pleased to have had some entries that have been written by children with a learning disability. We even have a story written to be signed as a conversation in Makaton.

We have made the decision not to alter the grammar of these stories. They may be slightly difficult to read in parts, but you are genuinely reading the authors voice.

I'm really grateful for the work of the teachers involved in the various schools that helped inspire children to enter their stories.

There is however, one slightly depressing thing that is worth mentioning:

In almost 50% of stories we received, the characters were bullied because of wearing glasses. This doesn't mean that the authors have had first hand experience in this bullying, but it does mean that this is what children think might happen. Glasses still hold some negative connotation in young people's minds.

When I first started out as an Optometrist over 20 years ago, I used to find that children were upset when they found out they needed glasses. Over the years I thought this had changed. Many of my patient's are excited when they find out they need glasses because nowadays glasses are trendy. Glasses are cool, aren't they?

Now more than ever we have wide choice of glasses, in every colour and shape imaginable. We have celebrities and YouTube stars wearing glasses and still children are being picked on because they need a medical device. I guess unfortunately it is same old story that when you are younger, being different to the crowd makes the crowd nervous, and they react to that.

What this means to me is that we still need us as Optometrists to try and fight some of this negativity and ignorance and this story competition has inspired me to do more. Glasses are not some sign of weakness or infirmity, neither are they a sign of intelligence. They are just a device that allows someone to see the world clearly.

But back to these fantastic stories.

I hope that all our authors are proud when they see their stories in print. They should be. I hope it inspires them to bigger and better stories. So, reader, keep this book safe. One day it might be worth a lot of money when one of these young authors receive their first booker prize.

Part 1:

Winning Entries

It took a lot of debating, a lot of thought and a lot of difficult decisions, but in the end these first six stories were the ones to truly capture our imaginations, and our hearts.

First place:

The Tragic Tale of Jake the Snail

By Jayden Vierra

About the Author:

Jayden is 9 years old and a pupil at St. Joseph's. His story is inspired by the idea that you can befriend anyone, and that there is nothing bad about getting glasses.

As his prize, Jayden's story has been illustrated and brought to life by Tim Cole.

He also received a pair of sunglasses from Simon Berry Optometrist.

The Tragic Tale of Jake the Snail

By Jayden Vierra

My name is Leon. This is a story about a determined boy (me) with glasses, and a more than exceptional snail, whose bravery will be remembered. Are you comfortable? Sit tight and listen.

I had trouble with my inexceptional eyesight, which caused me to not do any fun stuff like sport, cooking, etcetera etcetera. Preposterous. Absolutely preposterous. In my house, there are always chores to be done. Although luckily I got out of doing chores round the house, which was awesome!!!

AWWW Leon!?

But every dog –or boy-- Has his day. This was mine. The last straw. It came to its peakiest point when I set my best clothes on fire. Crazy, you don't have to tell me! I was reaching for the delicious frothy hot chocolate up in the top drawer. I leaned over the oven, and set my clothes on fire.

While mum put me out, she screamed, "Next time (if there is one) you should be more careful!"

I was scarred for life - literally - I have a scar down my left eyebrow.

Well, let's get back to the point. We went to the old opticians, which was down the street opposite the local burger bar. (For the record, the owner of the opticians <u>hated</u> burgers.) Next door to the burger place there was a pizza shop, but it didn't sell much, because not even a pizza could compare to a delicious burger with bacon... But, we're getting off the point.

So, anyway, the old lady that owned the optician was crazy, and she told crazy stories as well.

OPTOMETRIST

I chose my glasses, bronze slices with a grape purple outline.

They looked crazy, but when I put them on, they were something different. It was good different. It felt like my eyes hadn't opened this wide for a long time. It didn't feel like 20 20 vision (it was though!). It felt like 40 40 vision.

The optician's crazy voice whispered "Beware, for those glasses are highly unstable."

I said, "Okay, but I'm still taking them."

As soon as I left the opticians, I saw a <u>starving</u> snail outside of Dominos demolishing a full stuffed crust pepperoni pizza with a side of garlic bread. I could even see the crumbs of pepperoni on his cheeks. (I befriended him and called him Jake.)

A few days later, from three miles away, I saw a poster.

You might think three miles is a bit too far, but for me, with my new glasses, it was like reading the poster from a metre away.

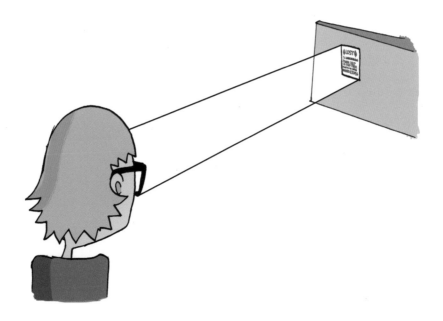

"We need to find these Lamborghinis, Jake, so we can buy more pizza," I exclaimed.

We looked for clues, and found a few suspicious fingerprints on the windows of several sports cars. With my glasses, it was obvious that they all belonged to the same person, who was keen on sausage rolls.

Not just any sausage rolls, but the new recipe vegan sausage rolls found only at the local bakery. (In my opinion, they're not the best. I prefer the non-vegan variety.)

I could see a clear trail of crumbs, leading directly to the bakers, and, of course, the culprit.

To test my suspicions, I decided to order a vegan sausage roll (the very last one) and to watch for his reaction.

He. Went. BONKERS!!

It began with a twitch of his eyes, which then progressed to his nose, before quickly escalating into screaming rage.

"GIVE ME THAT SAUSAGE ROOOOOLLLLLLLLLL!"

And with that, he began to chase me around the gingerbread man shelf.

Not for long though, as the culprit got caught in a trail of Jake's snail slime.

"I'll give you my vegan sausage roll if you give me the location of Her Majesty's stolen Lamborghinis," I demanded.

Stuck in the slime, he had no choice but to agree.

It was the last vegan sausage roll he tasted for a while.

I hope he enjoyed every last bite, as I don't think Greggs donate sausage rolls to jail.

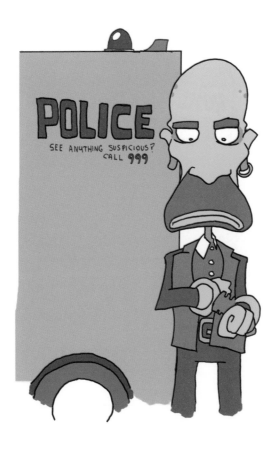

As for me and Jake, once we'd given the police the location of the stolen cars, we received our reward, and spent it on the biggest pizza party the world has ever seen.

(Honestly, it's in the Guinness Book of World Records.)

We even invited Her Majesty the Queen and she actually came.

She offered us jobs as her personal detectives, which we gladly accepted... or should I say *I* accepted.

It turned out that the Queen's eye-sight wasn't as good as I thought. As she bent down to congratulate Jake, I heard a fatal CRUNCH.

Jake was nothing more than fragments of shell, and a slimy puddle that was whisked away at once. But, his spirit is still with me, as well as my special glasses. And think I'll perhaps give the Queen the crazy old optician's business card. She could do with a test...

Second Place:

Ethel's Glasses

By Erica Leigh Snowball

About the author:

Erica is 8 years old and is a pupil at Nettlesworth Primary School. She loves to write stories and all of the characters come from Erica's own imagination and the adventures she has in the garden. Erica likes chocolate and Harry Potter.

As her prize, Erica received a year's subscription to the Durham Wildlife Trust.

Ethel's Glasses

By Erica at Nettlesworth Primary School

My best friend is called Ethel. She lives in our garden, in our bird bath. You might think that this is really silly but Ethel is a mermaid! If Ethel could stand up she'd be about 4 inches tall! She wears her hair in long red braids, she has a big round belly and when she smiles you can see she has no teeth! Ethel is quite unusual but she is perfect to me.

I was playing outside with Kate, my little friend unicorn, who lives in our pumpkin patch. I was throwing berries for her to catch when I heard Ethel crying.

"What's wrong Ethel? Why are you so sad?" I asked.

Ethel wailed... "I was watching you play catch with

Kate but.....but...but..... I couldn't see you properly! You were all fuzzy!"

I looked at Ethel as she continued to sob. "Ethel, does this happen a lot?"

"Yes," she said.

"My friend Betsy at school had to go and have her eyes tested when she couldn't see properly," I replied.

Ethel looked at me confused...... "Tested?"

"Yes Ethel," I replied.... "My mummy takes me to see a special man who tests my eyes. He is called an optician I think."

Ethel continued to cry. "Ethel you might need glasses. We should take you to the optician."

All of a sudden Ethel began to wail louder! "Ethel SHUSH....You will scare away the ladybirds screaming like that. And don't wake Fred up. You know how grumpy he gets when he is tired!"

But it was too late. Fred poked his head out of the fairy house window. "What is all that awful noise?" he groaned. "A fairy needs his sleep – it's hard work collecting teeth all night!"

"I am so sorry Fred, Ethel is crying and she won't stop!" I nodded in Ethel's direction.

Fred closed the window loudly then opened his door. Fred is a funny fairywith the brightest blue wings, he lives in out fairy house "Ethel, why are you crying?" he shouted.

"Because I don't want glasses!! Everyone will laugh at me! Have you ever seen a mermaid with glasses?" she cried loudly.

"Ethel lots of people wear glasses, don't be so silly. Even your favourite wizard Harry wears glasses. There's no need to cry," said Fred. I think Fred was a little bit cross at being woken up.

Mummy shouted me in for tea so I said goodbye to my friends and left them talking. As I was sat eating my tea

I asked my mummy if she could take Ethel to the opticians. My mummy rang them and we got an appointment for the next day.

In the morning I went to tell Ethel. She wasn't happy but she agreed to come. Taking a mermaid in the car is quite tricky, my Mummy filled up an ice cream tub with water and I sat with it carefully on my knee. Ethel thought it would be funny to splash me but she soon got told off by Mummy!

When we got there Ethel looked really sad. She told me that she was scared that the test might hurt. I told her it wouldn't but she still looked really worried. We sat and waited for our turn. Soon a nice lady shouted Ethel's name and we went into a room.

"OK Ethel, you are going to read the letters on this board and when you can't see them anymore just stop," she said.

Ethel confidently started shouting leters "A", "O"......

But soon Ethel stopped reading the letters. The optician did lots of tests but Ethel wasn't scared anymore, she was even giving us a gummy smile. At the end of the tests, the optician said that Ethel would need some glasses to be able to see properly. She found a lovely pair of round purple ones that would fit Ethel perfectly. Ethel screamed with delight "MY FAVOURITE COLOUR, I LOVE THEM!!"

All the way home Ethel was singing in the car about her new purple glasses, she was so happy.

"That didn't hurt at all!" she said.

After tea I went outside to see Ethel, Kate and Fred were playing in the pumpkin patch so I sat next to the bird table chatting with Ethel.

"How do you feel now Ethel? I think your new glasses are really pretty," I said.

Ethel grinned at me "I never realized how pretty the garden was before as I couldn't really see it. Everything is just so pretty. I love my new glasses. Thank you for taking me to the opticians."

Later that night Mummy tucked me in bed, as I laid there drifting off I could hear Ethel still happily singing about her new glasses. It's a good thing Fred was out doing fairy business or I think he would have been quite cross!

The end

Flash Fiction Winner:

Supergirl crash!

By Evie, Luke, James, Phoebe, Chloe and Brie

About the Authors:

They are from the reception class of St. Hilde's School.

As their prize, New Writing North donated 8 children's books to the nursery class.

Supergirl Crash!

Super Girl was flying in London City. She was low in the sky going around the buildings. She saw the big big shops below her. Suddenly she heard fighting in the shops! She used her superpowers to fly down to have a look.

"Oh no! My eyes are going blurry!" shouted Super Girl.

Crash, bang, wallop!

Super Girl bumped her head and fell onto the ground. She lay down still, she couldn't move. Boom supernan landed next to Super Girl. Superman picked her up and carried her to Simon Berry's opticians. Simon was shocked to see Super Girl and Superman.

"Oh my goodness gracious me!" said Simon.

Super Girl woke up and told Simon about her blurry eyes.

"Don't worry, I will help you," he said. He tested her eyes. "You need some glasses."

Super Girl said, "thank you for helping me. I love my new glasses."

So Super Girl and Superman zoomed off to help people in trouble!

Judge's choice:

No, no, no, I won't go!

By Martha and Susannah Child

About the authors:

Martha and Susannah are sisters. Martha is 13 and is an avid reader, enjoys playing the piano and using Makaton. Susannah is 11 and enjoys writing, gymnastics and learning history.

No, no, no, I won't go!

By Martha and Susannah

This is the story of a person who has additional needs and has to sign to communicate. They have been through many medical procedures and so are put off by the idea of hospitals and doctors. This story is a dialogue between a parent/carer and a child who does not want to go for an eye test. It could be shown with pictures and is simple and easy for for people with special and additional needs to sign.

We are going on a mission, to find the optician.

No, no no, I don't think so!

Just sit in the chair and have a long stare.

No, no no, I don't want to go!

Don't be a trickster, he will give you a sticker.

No, no, no, I won't go!

Just sign what you see, how hard can it be?

No, no, no, please don't make me go!

You will be fine, he can sign.

No, no, no, I really can't go!

He's got a special machine – you can watch the screen! See your favourite show, sing and dance as you go.

Oh! Yes, yes, yes, I will take the test!

Judge's choice:

Barney's adventure to Simon Berry's

By Tori Lee Cairns

About the Author:

Tori is 10 years old and a pupil at St. Josephs. Her story is about a beach trip gone wrong and overcoming bullying.

Barney's adventure to Simon Berry's

By Tori at St. Joseph's Primary School

One morning, I was eating breakfast then my mum (Anne, 32, loves going to beach) shouted "Barney it is time to go to the beach!" today was my birthday; I was 11. I ran upstairs to get dresses and my dad (Phil, 42, loves driving) roared "we are in the car!" I grabbed my lunch box and dashed to the car. Off we went.

When we got to the freeing beach I went to swim in the sea because the sun shone on the water. Then, I dried myself of and went to play with Pippin (dog). We played fetch. It started to get colder and windier. It wasn't the right day for the beach.

Sand was blowing. Everywhere. It got in my eye. As soon as we got home we rinsed my eye. It wouldn't stop hurting. It was terrible.

"My mum questioned, "are you still in pain?"

"Yes!" I replied.

Struggling, I tried to read my book, it was hard so my mum booked me an appointment at Simon Berry's. At first I didn't want glasses but I got them anyway. When I went back to school, I got bullied by Stephanie and Albert. They are so mean to everyone, they called me four eyes. But two months later Stephanie went for an eye test at Simon Berry's and got glasses. One week ago they snapped my glasses.

Can you guess what? I went back to Simon Berry's but they told me I didn't need glasses anymore. The next day they were very kind and we made friends. If you ever need glasses you should wear them because you might never need them again.

Judge's choice:

The Widdershins

By Tamsin Tyler-Wilson

About the Author:

Tamsin is 11 years old and a pupil at St. Josephs. Her story is about how unique and special glasses make you and when wearing them you can transform into anyone you wish.

The Widdershins

By Tamsin at St Joseph's Primary School

My name is Wendy and I am known as the immortal optician. I have seen eyes of many different colours and made glasses for many different people; too many to count. But at this moment a girl with eyes only seen once a century has just disappeared around the corner...

Earlier today I was sitting at my desk staring, pen in hand, at the large pile of papers to be filled out before tomorrow. I am and was dreadfully regretting not filling them out when I first got them. Just as I was pulling the first one towards me...

DIIIINNG!

Someone was at the door. Quickly, I stood up to open it, and was greeted with a rare sight.

Standing in front of me was a girl with a few striking features. She was short and had hair much longer than mine but her eyes stood out most of all. They reflected a galaxy beyond our own; a swirling trail of glittering stars sparkling their way across a dark velvety sea. I followed her as she ran to my bookcase, pushed one in and opened the door to my workshop. She was this month's Mina. She followed me as I led her down the stairs to my workshop. In there I can create glasses of many magical abilities depending on what shape they are and what metal. Mina's always come for transfiguration glasses.

My workshop is a room scattered with puffy armchairs and wooden workbenches with trays of lenses in all sizes and shapes. On one wall the shelves are full of normal, plastic glasses frames. On the other wall the shelves are full of different metals for magic glasses. As I scurried around Mina told me the same story as those before told me.

"My name is Mina Widdershins, and I know you know this but I must tell you anyway. I am here for your transfiguration glasses to disguise myself from those who want the galaxy for themselves. As you also know, if you are born in my family with these eyes you are automatically named Mina."

By the time she was finished, so was I. So she put the glasses on, got black hair and green eyes before disappearing around the corner.

Part 2:

The Judges' Shortlist

It was very, very hard choosing the winning stories from so many amazing entries... and the judges all had favourites that came very close! Here's all the stories that made someone's top 10!

Batman saves the day!

By St. Hildes School

Super Girl woke up late on Monday Morning. It was a beautiful sunny day. As normal, she used her super ears to hear any trouble.

"Oh no! There's trouble in Durham!" she shouted.

She put on her superhero clothes and zoomed to help. Super Girl went super fast to stop the people fighting but she was going so fast she crashed.

Crash, bang, boom!

She crashed onto the floor. She hurt her nose and her eyeballs stopped working. Batman came flying like a bat. He picked her up and took her to his batmobile. They drove to Simon Berry's opticians. Simon was sad to see Super Girl hurt.

"Are you ok? How can I help you?" asked Simon.

Super Girl said "My eyes are hurting. I crashed and bumped them."

"I think you need some glasses," replied Simon.

"I would like some rainbow glasses please," said Super Girl. "I think my friends will love them."

Super girl put on her new rainbow glasses and she smiled. Batman and Super girl zoomed off to help the people in trouble.

Harry and the Eye Test

By Jay at Trinity School

Harry was extremely scared for his first eye test. He hoped he'd not need glasses because he thought his dinosaurs and his friends would laugh at him. His mum said; "Harry we're going to the optician! Get on the bike."

Harry got his dinosaurs and got on the bike.

When they got to the optician Stegosaurus said: "Do us dinos need glasses, harry?"

"No, you don't need glasses," said harry.

The optician said "next!"

Harry and mum came in. T-rex said "this will be fun! I wish I saw what's going on."

Harry said "remember the magic button on my bucket."

"Hello Harry! I'm the optician, but you can call me Mr. Sight."

Mr Sight started to look at Harry's eyes but Harry pressed the button on his bucket and all of his dinosaurs grew bigger and bigger and bigger. Mr Sight said "Wow! I'm shocked!"

Harry said "it is quite nice." Harry pressed the button again and all off his dinosaurs shrank then went back in the bucket.

After the appointment Harry went to change into his pajamas and went to bed. Harry was glad he did not need glasses!

The next day Harry went to school. His friends asked about the appointment. Harry said it went fine and he does not need glasses. His dinosaurs were happy too. There was an assembly about sight and unexpectedly Mr. Sight came and called Harry up. He told the students how brave he was and everyone cheered.

The end

Cure for Blindness

By Adam at St. Joseph's Primary School

For James, everything was blurry and extremely fuzzy. His favourite thing to do in all the universe was to read, and he was amazing at it, but on this weird day he found it impossible to read. He was the best reader in his school, even though he was only in year 4, but for now he couldn't rad a single word. This was okay, since it was in the summer holidays, but it still exasperated him and made him absolutely mad. I mean extremely mad!

When he was having his breakfast, James said to his mum, "everything is incredibly blurry and infuriatingly fuzzy which makes it impossible for me to read!"

"We need to go to the opticians to get your eyes tested," replied James' mum calmly, "we'll go as soon as they are open."

"I can't wait to read again!" shouted James enthusiastically. As soon as he finished his breakfast, which consisted of porridge, he dashed to his room ready to get ready to go to the opticians, bumping into a door in the process.

Minutes later. James and his mum were outside of their white, plastic door which you had to slam if you were closing it. They dashed to the opticians to get the first appointment of the day. They got there in one minute flat.

"In you go," said the receptionist, while herding James and his mum into a room which had glasses covering its walls.

Ten minutes later, when the optician who was always smiling his smile which connected his ears in one big upturned arch had chosen the perfect glasses for James, the optician announced "I know what you need!"

He elegantly grabbed some glasses with ridiculously minute lenses which made James wonder who would have the patience to fit the minute glasses into the equally tiny frame. The frame was onyx black with what actually looked to James like splodges of paint, but which were actually pieces of azure fossilized into the onyx frame. He knew everyone in his class would laugh at him because of his glasses but he didn't let that bother him. Because of his glasses, which made him want to read, he and his mum didn't stay any longer than needed.

On his way home, James' eye was caught by the most peculiar sign ever. It said this:

Needed
Cure for blindness.
Reward: £12,000,000,000

The next second, a black limousine drove up and an anonymous man grabbed James by the arm and pulled him inside the pitch black car.

"as you saw on the sign, we NEED a cure for blindness!" said the man who had forced James into the car.

"AND WHAT DO YOU WANT FROM ME!?" replied James angrily.

"Of course, we need the cure, and the reward could be yours," said the man.

"Meet me here tomorrow and tell me what the cure could be!" answered James, as he climbed out of the black limousine, which also had dark windows.

***

The next day, at precisely 6am, James had arrived at he place the sign was(I wrote was, because it had been removed). A sleek black car pulled up and a window was removed, and then a man shouted for

James to get in the car.

From inside the car, the world was a giant labyrinth of signs trying to confuse the driver. There was one tunnel with one sign saying:

Volcano of Sight

The tunnel itself was charred and hot.

"That," announced the driver, "is where we're going!"

And they went speeding. I don't recommend Labyrinth travel to you if you're afraid of:

- the dark
- heights
- the deep
- quick changes between height and depth

or if you don't like

- hot weather
- cold weather
- quick changes between the two.

In other words, it was not that bad for James. But back to the story, James could only use the car to go at supersonic speed for the tunnel was a dead end.

"You have to get out to continue your quest," announced the driver. "I'll pick you up in 24 hours from here. Antonio, keep James safe."

A black hound, big enough to ride on, bounded over to James and started licking his face.

"Antonio!" groaned James. "Let's go!"

James athletically jumped onto Antonio's back. Antonio bounded towards the wall and ran right through it. It was a bumpy ride for James. (To be precise, it almost broke his bum bones.) The air grew hotter each second, as they were dashing towards Mt. St. Helens.

The scorched walls, which looked as though they were made from compressed ashes, became a blur, as they sped towards a faint glow. James still felt like his bum bones were cracking apart, but he endured the pain.

They burst out of a tunnel and into a cavern (the magma chamber of Mt. St. Helen's after it blew itself apart) and James saw that it was nearly full of magma. Anyway, there were wire bridges spanning across the cavern. Where the bridges met, a cauldron filled to the brim with lava and a substance, which I am going to call Greek flames as it was constantly burning with green flames, was located. Next to the cauldron were two carts filled with onyx black metal and bronze.

"BURN! Burn the two!" boomed an invisible voice from the cauldron.

"Don't burn me!" screamed James.

"You need to burn the two materials!" boomed the voice, and it never spoke again.

Normally, James would never do such a thing, but he did this anyway: he dashed across a bridge, even though it was on the verge of collapsing. He luckily made it across the bridge. He grabbed some bronze and onyx metal and dumped them into the cauldron, but nothing revealed itself. James had absolutely no idea what happened. He didn't have much thinking time (to be precise, he had just one second) as he noticed that Antonio belly-flopped into the magma and paddled across to James. Antonio put his nose into the Greek flames. James realized he needed to tip the bronze and onyx into **just** the Greek flames.

With Antonio's help, James tipped four heavy carts of material into just the flames. Suddenly, a green and white orange with eyes of azure majestically emerged from the place the flames met the lava.

"Blindness! Shall! NOT! Rule!" boomed the orange in the deepest voice imaginable(maybe even a little bit deeper).

"Finally! WE HAVE THE CURE!" exclaimed James as he

grabbed the orange of vision. James took off his glasses, because he was so happy, but quickly put them back on, as he couldn't see a thing.

James turned round to go, but disaster struck; the bridge they came from had collapsed. Now some good news – there were three other bridges. They chose the bridge to the left of the collapsed bridge. James and Antonio dashed across it just before it collapsed too. James told Antonio to go to the right, since they were to the left of the tunnel they came from. As they stepped into the tunnel, they mysteriously appeared in the place they would be collected.

***

One hour later, they were sitting in the black car. As the engine started, space and time curved, and in five quick minutes, the cure was delivered to Her Majesty the Queen.

"Here is your reward," said the Queen as she opened a secret safe in her throne which hid a nearly infinite supply of money. "And do you want to know what made people blind in the first place? A radioactive fart!" she announced.

***

At James' house, James' mum said, "good to see you again, vision-returner-James. Do you know what you want to spend the reward on?"

"Yes," answered James with a smile. "I do."

And so, the moral of the story is don't be scared to get a pair of glasses. They open up the door to new worlds – perhaps literally, if you pick a pair like James!

My Short Story

By Katie at Belmont Community School

Kayla was 10. She had secretly always wanted glasses but was worried about what her classmates would think. When the day of her eye test finally came she was really nervous but excited at the same time. The friendly man asked her questions about her eyes and made her wear some funky looking glasses too. After the test was over the man told Kayla's mum the results...

She would need glasses! Oh no! Thought Kayla, this is what she didn't want. However, when Kayla and her mum went to chose her new glasses she felt weirdly relaxed. There were so many different types of glasses but one pair looked so unique and different that Kayla was drawn to them instantly. Kayla asked her mum if she could get them and she said yes. Kayla was so happy and couldn't wait to try them on...

Kayla lifted the glasses to her face and put them on. Suddenly,

Kayla felt this magical feeling wash over her, Kayla was confused because her mum was screaming and shouting and she didn't know why. Kayla turned her head to look in the mirror and realised what was wrong... she was invisible!

The Mysterious Blob

By Charlotte at St Joseph's primary school

Millie stared. Harder than she had ever stared in her life. She saw a large pitch black splodge on her bright, pink bedroom wall. She was awfully confused as she could always see things very well. She stomped down the wooden staircase hoping her mum was home so to check. She screamed from the top of the stairs, "Mum are you home?" But she heard no response...

It turned out her mum was at the pharmacy getting some contact solution for her bad eye sight. Meanwhile Millie was lying in her bed watching The Titanic. "OUCH!!!" Millie screamed as she felt a slight sting on her left hip . (little did Millie know the sting on her hip was caused by the blurry black splodge on her wall...)

"You know what? I'm going to go to my best friend Lola's house. Maybe she will come to the optician with me as I can't see anything black," she screamed as she slammed the door.

Finally Millie arrived at Lola's house. While she was walking up the drive, she saw the black thing she saw earlier that morning again!

"UGH what is this? Why can't I see this mysterious splodge?" Millie said loudly.

Lola's mum answered the door and said, "Hello Millie. Are you okay? you look a bit down in the dumps."

"Yes I'm fine thanks for asking. Anyway is Lola home, can I come in and play?" Millie asked politely.

"Of course you can!" said Lola's mam.

She ran up to Lola's room.

"Oh? Hi Millie. What are you doing here?" questioned Lola.

"Um..... I don't really know how to say this but this morning, I saw a blurry black splodge on my wall then something stung me then I saw the blurry thing again. The point is will you come to the optician with me please, please, please?" begged Millie.

"Urrrrrr..--. Sure I will!"

Lola and Millie were on their way to the opticians for her

appointment when Lola said out of no where, "What do you think that black thing could have been?"

"Hmmm I'm not really sure to be totally honest with you," Millie explained.

"Okay, we'll soon find out!" Lola said positively.

The two girls shortly arrived at the opticians so they sat in the waiting area until they got called in. Then they heard a deep voice, "Millie Andrews?" It was the optician.

"Yep, that's me!" Millie told him.

"Good day Millie, I'm Doctor Foster the kids optician but you can call me doc!" he said.

"Hmmm... it seems you can't see anything that's black. That's a very rare case of NOBLACKILITIS!" Doctor Foster said in shock.

"Is that bad?" Millie asked hoping it was alright.

Then Doctor Foster said, "Yes it's fine you just can't see anything that's black so take these supervision glasses and then you should be able to see everything super clearly again!"

"Okay thanks Doc!" Millie said as she left the building.

"Hey Lola I'm going to head off home because it's school

tomorrow, bye!" shouted Millie as she waved goodbye.

"BYE MILLIE SEE YOU TOMORROW!" Lola bellowed from across the street.

***

It was a warm and sunny Monday morning and Millie was getting ready for school. She could see amazingly as she got some snazzy new glasses and she could see black things again!

"MAM, I'M LEAVING FOR SCHOOL!" Millie yelled up the stairs.

Just as Millie was leaving her mum shrieked "Come here, Millie I need to see what you're wearing because I don't want you breaking the school dress code again!"

"it's okay mum I'm only wearing my teal dress I'm fine. Goodbye mum!" Millie scowled

"Okay bye honey have a nice day!" Mum replied

Millie was stood nervously in the dark school hallway(she was nervous because of what she was wearing. It was a big change as she always just wore a grey T-shirt and black school pants) She was wearing her sapphire coloured specs(glasses), a crepe coloured lip gloss and a teal and turquoise dress. Everybody was staring at her

67

weirdly she was so embarrassed.

"What was that!?" Millie asked Lola.

"I'm not sure wait it's a...a...a SPIDER AAAAAAHHHHHH!!!"
Lola screamed

"Oh no! That's what the blurry black thing was!!!" Millie
discovered.

**PERHAPS 2020 VISION HAS
SOME NASTY HORRORS IN STORE FOR US!
HA HA HA!!**

The Blind Pianist

By Kacey at St Joseph's Primary School

Once there was a boy called Jamie and he loved to play the piano in his room as much as he could, and hoped to perform one day so everyone could hear his talent. The only thing stopping him was he was only 10 years old so he had a lot of time to wait and practice.

Skip 13 years, now Jamie is amazing at the piano. He didn't just do covers of songs anymore, he wrote his own songs now too! His money grew as he sold out at concerts and had enough people listening to him to fill a football stadium. His dreams and wishes had come true. By now he had done about 30 concerts and the money he would make he would donate to blind people. Everybody loved him and was inspired by him. They would do anything to get his tickets, they would also donate to blind people too now.

One day he went to the beach with his family. His Mam, Tessa, his dad, David, and his little sister Katie. It was a beautiful day. The sun was shining, the the crystal clear water was sparkling and glistening in the sunlight. Katie was playing in the ocean. Meanwhile Jamie was sunbathing next to Tessa and Daniel until this happened...

All of a sudden the sun shone brighter than ever all Jamie could see was many, fuzzy black smudges in his eyes. He told his mum and she told him to stop lying as he usually jokes around. They got Katie out of the water and went home.

The next morning Jamie went to the opticians.

Already he missed colour and longed for blue or purple or pinky yellow, or anything that wasn't black and fuzzy. Even brown brown would do. He had to try on almost every pair of glasses at the opticians but finally he found the right pair. He pushed them up the bridge of his nose. Jamie held his breath. What if he was still blind? What if he could never play piano again?

He opened his eyes slowly and gasped. Colour filled his vision. He had never been so amazed to be able to see. The family got home and Jamie sprinted to his piano. He had never experienced his vision so much. He went to sleep after a hectic day.

***

The following morning, Jamie woke from his slumber, and

couldn't see anything. He reached and felt for his glasses and realized he already had them on. HE HAD GONE EVEN BLINDER! He ran downstairs and told his mum. They went out to a restaurant to clear their minds. A little girl a couple of tables away who was also blind came up to Jamie and started talking.

"You're blind too aren't you?" said the little girl.

"Yeah, and I hate it."

They chatted for a little while, they learned each others' names. Jamie met Chelsea's guide dog, Gallop. She had helped him memorise the piano now. And he could finally play again.

The Sight

By Millie at Belmont Community School

Eyes. Something we all take for granted, until they are taken away.

She woke up, her dream fading as she sat up in bed. Something was different. Her eyes wouldn't open, she couldn't see. When her eyes eventually opened, she didn't see her room. She was in a huge double bed, and across the room was a window that stretched from the floor to the ceiling.

She got out of bed and walked over to the window. Outside was a huge, dark lake. But the lake wasn't calm, it raged like the ocean. Huge waves crashed against the banks and white horses raced up the hills, hoping to be free. This wasn't her home, not at all. But it seemed strangely familiar. She rubbed her eyes, but the lake was still there when her eyes opened again.

She walked to the window on the other side of the room. The longer she looked, the more people she could see. They were moving insanely fast, they couldn't be human. She walked to the door and left the room.

She padded down the stairs and expected to see her mum waiting for her with a glass of orange juice and a slice of toast, but that wasn't what she saw. The kitchen was full of people in black, leather clothing. They were sharpening huge blades on a block that sat on the counter.

She stood and stared, her fiery red hair falling into her face. As if they could sense her presence, two people turned and stared. They walked over and smiled.

"It's so good to see you again, Layla," the girl said.

"Who are you?" Layla asked, baffled.

"You don't remember us?" the boy asked, obviously hurt.

Layla fell to the floor, her eyes welled with tears. "I just want to go home," she whispered.

"But this *is* your home, Layla," the girl said softly.

Layla closed her eyes and hoped that when she opened them again she would be at home.

Glasses Girl

By Mae at Belmont Community School

I walked into the opticians, my brow dripping with sweat.

I was very nervous- what would my friends say? I am going into year 7 soon... I can't be seen with these! Hnng... but I have no choice. I have to have them because my mum will make me. She'll glue them to my face if she has to.

While basically having a meltdown, I stared around the room. I saw small children- probably around the age of 6. Would they feel bad about having glasses? Probably not.. They wouldn't have to put up with being judged.. Kids at that age don't really care about looks do they? They just wear whatever their mums or dads pick out for them and go about their day. Just then, I heard someone shouting my name. It was time to get my glasses.

I came out better than expected. My glasses were alright, SPECtacular even(haha see what I did there?). There's a little secret about my glasses.. I think I can see the future! I haven't told anyone yet because with great power comes great responsibility! Or maybe great evil.. MWAHAHAHAH!! Ah well maybe not..

Things I've seen already are: an ice-cream van, a birthday party and some not so great things. I saw a bank robbery.. Wait.. Maybe I could stop these things! Mae Stephenson, superhero extraordinaire! Glasses Girl! Or maybe I'll just stick to using it for homework.. For now at least. I am only 13 after all.

Watch out future, I'm on my way!

Doctor of Disappearance

By Sam at Belmont Community School

It was March 23rd, my 13th birthday. The chair I was laying back in was less than comfortable. The doctor entered. He had something reminiscent of a of a welding mask covering his face. He was wearing black trousers, a white shirt and a long, black shotgun coat.

Without uttering a word he took a pen looking object off of his apparatus wall. He held it above my eye. A small rotating dial was set into the side of the object, it was set to max setting. Without warning, the doctor clicked the pen and half of my vision was turned red.

There was no pain, just an uncomfortable feeling of something trying to burrow into my eye. The burrowing went further and further into my eye until it ended up at the back of my eye.

A loud click echoed around the room and the redness disappeared. The same happened with the other eye and by the time the redness disappeared the doctor had disappeared. I stood up from the chair and everything was grey. It was all getting darker. Frightened, I stumbled out of the room and felt the warm air on my face. The broken buildings that many called home were slowly disappearing. Then it all went. The rubble on the streets, the bombed buildings, everything had gone.

I jumped when a hand rested on my shoulder, "Take this," a voice said in my ear.

I was handed what felt like a glass and a small ball. With the ball rested on my tongue, I gulped down water and slowly my vision was slowly coming back. A blue sky was developing. Then buildings of every colour sprouted out of every street. This wasn't the world I knew, or the world I wanted to live in. Overcome with every feeling I could possibly feel, I fell. I hit my head on the pavement and everything went black.

I woke up, I was in my bed. Everything was normal. My phone buzzed and I picked it up. Opticians appointment in an hour.

I convinced myself it was all going to be okay and stood up.

The Eye of Resistance

By Davy at Belmont Community School

The apocalypse was full throttle. No one could stop it, or maybe they could. The prophecy said this would happen but it also said the one who was resistant to the virus could save the world.

We just need to find out who it is.

Clifford and I walked outside hoping to be alone but we weren't that lucky. There were 3 of them. Hungry. Diseased.

"Damn!" I exclaimed, "we left our guns inside."

"Let's kick ass old school," whispered Clifford.

I picked up a plank of wood from the floor, positioning the weight perfectly in my palm. I swung back and flung the wood at the middle zombie, skilfully knocking him out. Clifford ran at the zombie on the right and powerfully drop kicked him knocking his loosely fitted arm clean off.

But while watching Clifford I was stupidly distracted and forgot about the third zombie. I felt an arm clasp my shoulder and then a sharp pain in my neck.

I had been bitten!

"Ahh!" I screamed. Clifford sprinted towards me with furious eyes and clobbered the zombie, placing him unconscious. Clifford stared at me and gawped.

"What?" I asked.

"Your eyes... they're glowing," he whispered, "you are the resistant one."

"No I can't be. I can't be the one to save the world." I mumbled, "l can't do it."

"Yes you can and I know how."

We drove for 30 minutes. Finally we stopped outside an opticians. "What are we doing here?" I asked.

"You'll see."

We went inside Clifford took me to a room with this big

machine with a huge lens.

"Sit down," he asked.

I did as he said and sat under the machine. "Now. You know how your eyes glowed when you were bit? Well... We are going to have you face into this giant lens and your eyes are going to shine into the lens and make a huge resistant cloud that will cure everyone."

"Woah."

"Well, are you ready to save the world."

"No, are *we* ready to save the world?"

Clifford clicked a button on the machine and a large buzzing noise filled the room. A laser shot out of the machine and into the sky creating a huge green cloud.

"It's working!" Clifford shouted.

10 minutes later we walked outside and saw real life humans. No zombies.

We had saved the world.

...My eyes opened and I sat up in my bed. "It was just a dream." I got out of bed and went downstairs. I walked over to my mum and said "I'm ready to get my eye test."

Blackbeard

By Dan at Gilesgate Primary

Part 1: The Cave

I, Blackbeard, am your regular pirate: A ruthless, formidable tyrant with gold galore and a beard as dark as many midnights but I have a fatal flaw, my choice of a glass eyeball. I will kill you, steal from you and and destroy you, but of all pirates, you would never pick me to be the scariest.

I need a way to prove myself to be fearsome, a distinguishing feature and I know where to find one. I'm at the most plundered part of this cruel world and about to test my recently plundered diving bell.

At the bottom of the sea, I can see stripped wrecks everywhere but not what I want. Bottles of rum, sand and cannons. Nothing. First mate Bob, Quartermaster Jeff and I take cannons, wood and iron to reinforce the ship because we can't bear to go back empty-handed.

On the deck, we hand over the items, barked orders at the crew and set sail for a couple of miles, where we dived back down into the murky depths.

Down, down, down. It seemed as if we were trying to descend into a fathomless pit. But surely enough, we reached the dark, shark-infested bottom. A gaping cave, darker than my beard, had been carved into the side, beckoning us to come in. We obliged. There was some sort of magical presence, we thought as we stumbled in. Was it one of us, or in there?

Part 2: The Map

As we entered, the magical feeling intensified and soon we could not feel anything else: our cuts and bruises, the rocks stabbing at our feet nor could we feel the weight of the diving bell. We just wanted to find the treasure that obviously would be there. Our pirate greed for all things shiny egged us on.

Little did I know that this treasure would change my life forever.

Eventually we came to a place and noticed that there was no water, so we took off the bell and threw it into a corner and gasped. Mother-of-pearl caskets, diamonds and other jewels met our eyes.

"Pinch me. I must be dreaming," I mumbled out of a gaping mouth.

First mate Bob pinched me.

"Yeouw! Why'd ya do that! Are you mutinous?" I shouted.

"I ain't being mutinous, just followin' orders. Ya said pinch me so I did. He he he," Bob replied cheekily.

I didn't listen to his cheek. I had clapped eyes upon a map and three diving suits with oxygen tanks and a plan started to form in my head. I loaded treasure into the discarded bell and slipped on a diving suit. Bob and Jeff copied me, and we carried the bell up between us.

It was long and arduous but it was worth it.

As we got to the surface we saw a huge sea battle raging. The Forever Adventure against... HMS Destruction, my old mutinous first mate Felix's ship. He had quit on piracy and joined the Royal Navy. Idiots in all other pirates' opinions. I drew my trusty cutlass and tore a gaping hole in the hull of his ship, then left and told my ship to set sail.

The map was curious. I had a miniature picture of the Adventure Forever which seemed to be moving with the ship. The course that I had plotted was taken from the dotted line on the map. It had the name of the treasure I wanted on it and that was the only reason I followed it.

It also had a riddle on the back:

Take this map, if you dare
For only the chosen one can move it
he will not be your normal pirate
but Strange,
and with a right to seek the treasure.

It all seemed to refer to me so I would not be... cursed?

It certainly seemed like a pirate curse. Anyway, we were nearing our destination, so I hid the map. I knew the place. It was the Bermuda triangle.

Then a cannonball hit our boat.

The HMS Destruction was here for more.

Part 3: The Treasure

Our new reinforcements were holding out well against these attacks, when all of a sudden, the HMS destruction disappeared entirely and a great hulking brute that I recognized as a Leviathan reared up out of the water.

"At least we have a couple less enemies ain't we now?" I shouted to Bob. "And one more!" I added as the Leviathan lunged towards us, but before I could so much as fire a cannon, my map shot out of its hiding place like a ninja star. I didn't see what happened but the beast collapsed a second later, clearly dead. Excitedly, I hurried down to reach my goal.

That was how I found the Golden Eyeball.

It had extreme magical properties, such as making the wearer have night vision, sight with both eyes and pinpoint accuracy with a pistol. I have decided that from now on, I will only attack a ship at night when they can't see, but I can.

This is the best item I have ever obtained!

Mortal Danger

By Amelia at St Joseph's primary   school

One rainy day in the tiny town called Sunnyside, a fifteen year old boy called Edward was in the cramped living room of his small, old and very cramped house. You might think that a town called Sunnyside would be full of happy and excited people making sandcastles on the sandy beach on a boiling, sunny day but it was the complete opposite. The fifteen-year-old boy who I was talking to you about earlier, well, that's me about ten years ago. There wasn't much to do in Sunnyside and there wasn't many kids there but me and my eight-year-old brother(Elliot) so I was in my living room playing videogames in front of our small TV- again.

"Mam! The wifi's gone again!" I shouted.

I loved my mam but she did get quite annoying when she always replied to my complaints, "Why don't you play a board game with your brother instead of whining about the wifi?"

My mam always worked so hard for me and her main priority was to make me and Elliot happy so I didn't want to be mean to her.

"OK mam, I'll play with El. Elliot?" I finally agreed. El was what I called Elliot for short. Unenthusiastically, I got up to play with my brother. Because I knew he'd throw a huge fit he didn't, I let him win all three games we played. After we both got bored of playing, we tidied up and went to get dinner. At the table, Dad said, "Edward, we're worried about your sight, all you do is sit in front of a screen."

"And?" I questioned, though I knew what he was about to say. "We're going to take you to Dr. Mark for a checkup, Son."

Dr. Mark was an optician with a lot of mysterious rumours about him. People had suspicions that they saw him in old photos of the opticians or some people think that he's been the shop's owner all along. I have to admit, all the rumours did make me kind of scared of him. I decided that if I had to go then I may as well investigate. Hopefully, I wasn't being rude, investigating his life.

When we arrived at the opticians, I got straight into my appointment. I asked him questions like "What was your grandad like?" and "How long have you been working here?" His answers seemed quite normal. Trying to act low-key, I asked other people in the waiting room about their suspicions. Eventually, it was time to go home.

At home, I began putting all my information together. As I sat at my desk, I began to think that I was being crazy. For about five hours, I was searching books about mythical creatures. There was information about wolves, elves, vampires and other strange, mythical creatures. Noticing that my investigating was starting to get out of hand, I tidied up and went to bed.

The next morning, I was still curious. Looking at what I had already investigated, the pieces started coming together. Could Dr. Mark really be immortal? No, he couldn't. That stuff was what happened in movies; not real life! Was I really getting to something or was I out of my mind? As quick as a flash, I ran downstairs and told mam that I was going to the park with my friends. "Can I come?" asked Elliot.

"No, El. It's just me and my friends," I replied, trying not to act suspicious. Quickly, I ran out of the house. I wasn't really going to the park – I was going to the opticians.

Finally, I arrived. Looking around for Dr. Mark, I walked around the opticians. Questioningly, people looked at me, wondering what I was looking for. "Are you looking for someone?"asked the receptionist.

"Um, actually, I'm looking for Dr. Mark. Do you know where he is?" I slyly asked.

"He's in the corridor," replied the receptionist. Eager to get more information, I walked into the corridor. "We can't just move away now, people will get suspicious," I heard Dr. Mark say.

"But we have to keep the secret of immortality a secret," mumbled his sister.

"What? Immortals!" I whispered too loud do they could hear me.

Looking concerned, they quickly shushed me. "Listen, now you know this, you are in grave danger," Mark whispered. "The Swan family will be getting involved."

"The Swan Family?"

"The leaders of our kind. Go home, we'll figure something out to keep you safe," they answered. If the Swan family found out, they would take my sight away. Keeping their secret was their biggest law.

Lying in bed, I began to feel worried. How come in one day I was suddenly in danger of getting my sight taken away. Mark told me that Amelia- his sister who can read the future- will know when the Swan family will want to fight. Mark would invent something to distract Felix- the leader -so that he can explain to him that the secret would be kept safe.

The day had come.

Mark had invited me over his house to explain the plan. "I've made a pair of glasses that, when he puts them on, everyone around him will look immortal. While he has them on, I will explain everything," Mark explained. We carefully walked down to the field where the Swans would want to fight. We Waited in panicked silence.

All of a sudden, they came. "I brought you a gift, Felix. Some new glasses," said Mark calmly. Felix put them on. "Ah, you have brought a new immortal," Felix smiled. Mark began to explain everything and finished. Then, Felix found out. He wanted a fight, I knew it.

However, Amelia quickly stepped forward and showed him what his future would be.

Felix stepped forward and said "we surrender."

We then went home and continued into our- sort of -normal lives.

The Child that Needed Glasses

By Florence at St Joseph's Primary school

My name is Iris, I'm a 12 year old girl, and my mum wants me to have an eye test. I don't really want one. So now I'm going to the opticians stomping and dragging my feet, I really don't want to go.

***

Me and my mum have just got out of the optician's. It was better than I thought it would be. I asked my mum if I did well. She said "sort-of."

I asked, "what do you mean?"

"Well, you got most of the letters wrong."

I might need glasses...

Right now I am going to pick up my glasses. I'm getting black small ones with glitter.

***

I've got my glasses and I'm walking to school now. My best friend Lucy has gotten glasses. Thy are dark brown (that look black) and they are small. Today school wasn't so good. I loved my glasses when I first got them. Now, I don't like them. Today me and Lucy were walking down the corridor and Chip, Cipper and Cliff (the big bullies) made fun of our glasses.

Later, at break, Lucy told me it had happened to her as well. She seemed upset, I feel sorry for her, it now has happened to her twice. So we went to Mrs Blackberry (the head teacher) and we told them off.

She said to us that it doesn't matter what you look like so long as you can see and that you are happy. So that is what I'm going to do from now on.

Iris.

The kid who wanted glasses

By Esther at St Joseph's Primary School

06/08/19

Today, I am getting glasses. I live in Durham with my mum. My parents are divorced. I'm 9 years old and my name is Ella. I'm an only child and I'm so excited to get glasses.

15/08/19

Today, I went to the opticians and got an eye test. They said that I didn't need glasses but then thy gave me a call saying that there was a mix-up. So after all I needed glasses! I am so excited to show my teachers at school! I can't wait. I wonder what my friends in class will think. To be honest, I think I suit glasses.

04/09/19

My first day at school wasn't as I expected it to be. To be honest with you it wasn't great (as I got bullied). I'm feeling a bit down. They called me names like; nerd, ugly, they don't suit you and mean things like that. The mean girls -who bullied me- are called Emma, Abigail, and Sophie. They're the popular ones- who get what they want and think that they're the best. My mum lost her job so I have 2 problems now and I don't know what to do.

19/09/19

There was a nice boy today -called Callum- he helped me out by backing off the bullies. He is so nice and I asked him out. So now he is my boyfriend. He is one of the popular ones too but he is kind and has lots of money. He has a family business of his father's and hired my mum and gave us all some money.

15/08/39

My time as a child has gone quickly, and now it's 20 years later since the last time I talked to you. We have 2 kids and they are twins. Gave birth no more than a year ago today. A girl called Boo and a boy called John. Me and Callum are married and our 2 kids- Boo and John- have glasses. So I remind them every single day how beautiful they are with or without glasses.

My life with glasses

By Ewan

Once I was born the doctors saw I had 'different' eyes so they booked me into an eye test, at the time I was 3 years old. I was a little bit nervous but excited, at the opticians they said I had to wear glasses. I thought my friends were going to not like me because of that so I had a little think, and I did get glasses they were life-changing. I could see everything at school, and everyone liked me.

As I moved to Catterick Garrison people like me because of my glasses. I moved into year 4 and I broke my femur by my leg colliding with a girl on a park roundabout, at that point I was one of the popular in school at the time! Then I went into year 6 that was tricky because I was in a mainstream school at the time. To help me I had a TA that I knew for 6 years, but we are still friends to this day.

My first secondary school was very tricky for me because it was when I had anger issues. Some girls did not like me because I hated

95

them too, a group of boys made fun of me calling me "old man" because I grew grey hair when I was very little. That made me really sad and angry. Into year 9 and I bent a bone in my wrist that also made me popular but I was in LS until my move to another school, but nothing happened there except on the way to school one day we collided with a lorry.

Back into familiar territory Durham, year 10 is going well but I'm dealing my anger issues by meditation and keeping calm but now I do not like loud noises. I got that covered up by ear plugs, now I have new friends I feel comfortable in a new but old environment, I coped with all of this because of glasses and I still wear them today.

Mimi's Glasses

By Julia at St Joseph's Primary School

Let me tell you a story about a little girl called Mimi, a ten year old loving girl. She had bad eyesight. She loved the colour purple because it reminded her of the galaxy. She wished for a black and white cuddly kitten who would send her to sleep every night. One day, Mimi saw a splodge on her car seat, she wondered what it was, but it was just her phone. She wondered what happened! Why could she only see a blur?

Half an hour later Mimi told her beautiful big sister, Lilly, what had just happened. Lilly had crystal eyes the colour of the ocean and her bottom. She was 19. She had a powder white car. And she is the most popular girl in her college. Lilly took Mimi to the school opticians. The opticians took Mimi while Lilly went home.

Mimi started to cry and Lilly came to her.

"I NEED GLASSES!" Mimi sobbed.

"I will help you find the perfect pair!" Lilly said excitedly. "I like this pair."

She pointed at the crystal blue pair.

"Are they ok?" Lilly asked politely.

"WOW!" Mimi screamed.

She saw close up, she saw black hairs on the marble floor. She looked outside and she saw spiders in the emerald grass. "OMG I want them! GLASSES!" Mimi screamed.

Mimi put on her glasses and when school ended Lilly took Mimi to the museum.

The news spread that someone stole £10,000,000 from the museum.

Mimi looked through her magical blue glasses and saw a purple hair and a soggy chip. So, Mimi went to the chip shop and saw the lady who stole the 10,000,000 gold! It was beautiful.

When Mimi saw the lady who stole the 10,000,000 gold, she called the police. When the police came, they dragged the old lady on the floor, while Mimi went to the lady's cheese filled locker in the staffroom. Mimi grabbed the sparkling gold.

Mimi saved the entire world with her special glasses.

See, glasses are not bad. They are cool, and stylish! Yes they are heavy, and yes in summer your nose goes rose red but Mimi thinks they are cool, special and magical!

First Eye Test

By Shakthi

"So... James." Mum paused. "We have a surprise for you," she calmly said, trying not to get too excited. I was not happy to hear this because Mum's idea of a surprise is normally extra homework, which is probably the worst thing that could happen, chores or walking Gregory (our dog). After some thought, I was ready to inhale the speech that mum was about to blurt out.

"YOU ARE HAVING YOUR FIRST EYE TEST WITH YOUR NEW BABYSITTER!" she screeched, this time at the top of her lungs. 'at the top of her lungs' meant that the whole universe could hear!

And that's not even her loudest!

I shuddered. A babysitter? An eye test? I was frozen.

There was a knock at the door. "Oh, that must be the

babysitter," Mum said, gazing at the door.

"Wha- what?!" I replied.

Mum stood up and answered the door. She came in swiftly and was wearing a juniper-green sweatshirt and coal black ripped jeans.

After mum and dad left, Emily (the hideous looking babysitter) had a sinister grin on her face. She rambled around the house and then invited herself into Mum's room. She slathered makeup all over herself.

To be honest, she looked plain hideous!

I couldn't get any sleep that night. That face would <u>NOT</u> get out of my head! It looked HILARIOUS!!!

I managed to fall asleep, but shortly after I heard a nose, rummaging. Was it a thief? Was it mum and dad? Were they back already?

I ignored it and the next thing I knew, it was morning. Today was my eye test.

"GET READY YOU NINCOMPOOP!" Emily shouted as she stomped downstairs.

I didn't even know why she was my babysitter in the first

place! I put on my butter-yellow t-shirt and my grey worn out jeans. We drove to Simon Berry's in Emily's dusty red car.

I was expecting this place to be dark and dingy, but surprisingly it felt comforting, which was like home. Emily was texting someone called 'Lina'.

"James Bond!" the receptionist called.

I was pushed into a small room (around 3m long and 3m wide) and there was the friendliest person I had ever met! It was Simon himself! He put this thingy-me-bob against my eye , he told me to look at a holographic piece of card and asked what I could see. I said car but he said it was a tortoise, this made me laugh. I think he was offended.

My eye test was over!!!!

I could go on with a million more exclamation marks!!!!!

I did it! Before I didn't know why I was so scared!!!

Since Emily was being annoying trying to pick ugly glasses for me, I just simply punched her. I picked these black, glossy glasses and then it was finally time to go home.

Mum and Dad were finally back! "Mum, Dad! What do you think of my glasses?" I asked them, quite nervous.

"I... I umm... I LOVE THEM!" Mum said, loudly.

Dad reminded my mum. "<u>WE</u> love them!"

"Oh and honey, put your uniform on the ironing board for tomorrow!" she shouted as I ran upstairs.

I had school tomorrow!!! I was actually pretty excited to see how my friends would react.

"Dude, you look different! What is it? Did you get plastic surgery?" Shawn went on.

"Bruh, if you didn't notice, I GOT GLASSES!!!!!!!" I squealed, jumping up and down.

"Whoa! Calm down! You're gonna need stitches!" Shawn laughed.

***

Fast forward to 5 years later.

Now, I am walking along the pavement reading a book, Charlotte's web. It's like I have a superpower. I can read a book and look where I'm going at the same time. My vision is 'the best!' in the school's stadium. We have to give a welcome speech to the new students, I have a good idea what it's going to be.

There is a first time for everything. It's okay to be scared. Be yourself no matter what!

Glasses can't define me.

Colour

By Noah at St. Joseph's Primary School

Hello!

My name is Tom, but you probably know me as Hippie Sight or Rainbow Man but that's what **they** call me. I have two older brothers; they don't call me those horrible names, though. I like them, they like me. Or should I say liked?

The year is 1987, computers are used by the public for... almost everything. My Dad decided it would be a good idea to bring one home (as he recently got a job at Apple), but little did he know what carnage it would bring upon the household.

"Computer? What's that?" 3-year-old I said, while tilting his head.

"It's something that you do stuff on," he replied, while setting it up.

"What are you doing?" my mum asked while barging in to lean against the hallway wall.

"I'm setting the computer up for the boys," he replied.

"Don't you think..." she said then mouthed stuff that neither I nor my brothers could understand.

To make it more complicated my dad did the same.

"Tom," my dad gulped in fear. "You can't go on."

"What, why?" I spilled out, while my brothers were in absolute shock.

"It'll hurt your... You're just too young, okay!" he finally said in fear.

"Don't worry, Tom; we'll still play with ya," Gordon, the oldest of the bunch said.

I wish that sentence was true.

I really wish...

Not only was this hard, not able to play with my brothers

Gordon and Simon, but at school was very hard. One day at school I was chosen to paint a snail (the legendary snail Luther). I painted the shell blue and the skin orange along with red eyes.

This of course, caused me to be bullied.

Oh and to top it all off a week later, 5 days after my birthday, my parents told me that I was **colour-blind**, yay!

At first I thought this was a good thing.

Ah, but it wasn't.

The bullies continued and continued... but little did I know at the time that my charm would come soon.

6 years later in a Friday afternoon I was enjoying myself, watching TV, until...

"BREAKING NEWS!" the TV presenter yelled.

"Argh, loud, very loud!" I shouted, reaching for the remote.

"A £1000 artefact has just been stolen and no-one can find footprints, or fingerprints!!" the TV presenter then said.

"Ha, what great fake news!" I giggled.

"No, this is serious Tom," Simon replied, being dead serious. I was intrigued, as I could clearly see 2 very suspicious footprints lying in the corner.

"Hey, can I walk the dog early?"

"If you must," Simon replied.

***

Right, here I am. Walking my pug on lead and following footprints which could just be a figment of my imagination! Or... so I thought...

I followed them to this creepy looking warehouse with two guys in. one is bald the other has an afro. Me being a 10-year-old, I reached into my pockets and pulled out a 90s looking telephone. As soon as I dialled the infamous number (999), the dog barked. The noise acted like bait to the two guys, as soon as the first beat of the noise happened, the two guys ran towards me as if they were starving men seeing a huge plate of steak.

I look up, then ran as fast as I could. I swear at the that I was running so fast smoke was coming out of my old, muddy trainers. Then, of course...

I tripped. Luckily, I was able to press enter on the telephone, making the police department guy hear the two guys say a load of junk like "I'M GOING TO KILL YOU!" and "I HATE YOU!". Then they said a load of stuff which is not appropriate for a children's book.

The caller heard. Coming straight my way, with 2 cars.

***

"YOU WENT THERE WITH THE DOG?!" my mum exclaimed, probably waking up the whole street.

I ran then nodded as I was frightened I'd be punished.

Then there was a knock at the door. My dad answered, talking to the stranger. Then he turned to my mum, tilting his head, hinting that he wanted her to come to him. Then to leave me in our 90's kitchen.

They must've had the dog chipped, how else would they have known, I'd went there?

Oh well, at least I caught the robbers along with the police giving me a lift home!!

Then, my dad came out with something in his hand, but his face was stern. Stern like I'd just batted a baseball into his bedroom window. But then, the stern face faded away into a happy, proud face. I kind of smiled back, as if I was trying to make some depressed person happy. Before, I was too focused on his face to tell what was In his hand. But, now I could look what was in his hands. And to my surprise...

It.

Was.

Glasses...

"Eh?" I proclaimed. "Is that an insult or...?"

"Put these on," he insisted. I did so, to be met with LOADS of colours in places I never knew before! Before the wooden floor was purple, now it was yellow.

"Birch!" I yelled.

"Indeed, son."

I simply hugged him, tears welling up in my eyes which were red before, but were now blue! The sofa was red, yet it was blue before. It was like going into another dimension. I smiled, the tears dripping down my face...

From then on, things were different.

I became a detective when I was older with my colour-blindness being able to see footprints even in the dark. I was no longer bullied. I could go on electronics, since I had the vision. My brothers respected me lots. I got congratulated at school for my talents against those robbers!

When I was older my parents even gave me this strange thingy called a 'phone'. Who could have known that glasses would have been the key to life?

Zoe's Glasses

By Lily at St Joseph's primary school

Zoe was a ten-year-old girl who had bad eyesight. Really bad eyesight. It came the day that Zoe had to go and get her eyes tested. She was scared but her mum persuaded her to go. Zoe said, "Ok, I'll go." She had to go twice, and the second time she got glasses. Her glasses were nature themed (she loves nature) and when she got to school everyone laughed and made jokes about her.

"What... is there something different about Zoe?" whispered Rachel to Kate.

"Yeah haven't you noticed SHE HAS GLASSES! HA HA HA!!!!" Kate, who is always loud, shouted for the whole yard to hear. Everyone started to snigger. Zoe only had one friend, that friend was called Lola.

"Do I look weird... like odd weird?" asked Zoe.

"Weird, no. Odd, you always are."

"Ha, well isn't that a nice thing to say," said Zoe sarcastically.

***

Later that day... Zoe was crying at home.

"Come on now, time to go and get your new glasses," softly mum said.

"I'm an embarrassment," Zoe whispered.

"What? I didn't hear you darling," mum said.

"I SAID I'M AN EMBARRASSMENT!...... sorry," Zoe gave her mum a hug.

"It's ok," said mum.

Not long after, Zoe and her mum were at the opticians.

"Here are your new glasses Zoe," said the optician.

"Thank you," said Zoe.

"Are you going to put them on?" asked mum.

"Uuum, I'll wait," replied Zoe.

"Ok," said mum.

As soon as they got home, Zoe climbed into her tree house and put on the glasses...

"AHH!!! I... I... I can see far away and so close up," shouted Zoe. "Mum!"

***

The next day, at 5am in the morning, Zoe rang Lola. She couldn't sleep for thinking about her supersonic vision, and she just *had* to tell someone.

RING RING RING!

"Come on, come on, pick up... Lola yes!" Zoe said excitedly.

"H, h, hello. Who is this?" Lola yawned.

"It'sZoeandI'vegotnewglassesandIcanseefarawayandsocloseup!"

"And you woke me up just to tell me that?" yawned Lola again, sounding a little annoyed now.

"Yes! Because I don't think it's normal to see far away and close up. I'm talking baby-birds-in-nests-in-trees-waiting-for-a-worm close up. Is that normal?"

"No Zoe, that's not normal. You've been dreaming. Now let me go back to sleep."

Brrrrrrrrrrrr. The phone line was dead.

"Hello? Lola? Ugh," huffed Zoe.

Later (but still early) that day...

"Morning pumpkin," said mum.

"Morning mum," Zoe said with a yawn.

At school, Zoe saw Lola.

"Hey Lola! Morningl" shouted Zoe.

"Hey Zoe! Morning. What's up?" Lola asked.

"Nothing. Anyway, did you answer your phone last night?" asked Zoe.

"Yeah, I didn't know who it was," Lola was pondering, and trying to recognise the voice. "Why?"

"Um, just asking!!!" Zoe said suspiciously.

"Yeah but WHY?" burst Lola, digging for answers.

The school bell rang.

RING RING RING!!!

"Oh look the bell –got to go-- bye !" Zoe waved.

"Oh. Bye then."

Lola was angry because Zoe left her in the middle of the yard.

At the end of the day, Lola followed Zoe out of school. Lola's phone rang. Zoe turned around and at the last minute Lola hung up and hid.

"Phew." Lola was relieved.

Zoe went into the woods. Everybody was scared about the woods, but Zoe and Lola had made a den. Zoe went into the den.

"Aaaahhh!" Zoe screamed.

"What's wrong?" Lola ran into the den behind her.

"Why are you following me Lola?!?!" Zoe was terrified.

"WHY ARE YOU IN THE WOODS!!??" Lola screamed.

"Look, the reason I'm here is because of these. MY GlASSES. I TRIED TELLING YOU BUT YOU DIDN'T LISTEN!" Zoe took a breath and left.

RING RING!

"Hello?" said Lola.

"Hi, you're late... VERY LATE. YOU'RE GROUNDED, WHERE ARE YOU?" Lola's mum screamed.

"I'm coming," said Lola. "Bye." but by that time, Lola's mum had already hung up.

"Hi mum," said Zoe like nothing had happened.

"Hi," said mum.

"Um, mum... could I tell you something? Ok... When I put on my glasses, I can see far away and close up."

"Ok, umm. I think we should go and get your eyes tested again." Mum was worried because she didn't know if it was her eyes or the glasses.

"No, I don't want to go back!" and with that, Zoe ran away.

While Zoe had a rest from running, she saw a poster which said:

The Queen's crown has been stolen. If you find this, please return it, and in return, you will get f270,000. Come to Buckingham palace.

Thank you.

"Hmm, interesting. I'm hungry, I'm going to the bakery," Zoe said to herself.

At the bakery...

"Hi, I would like a sausage roll please," said Zoe.

"Here you go, that will be £1 please," said the shopkeeper.

"There. £1," said Zoe.

Zoe walked out of the bakery and saw a man with a backpack. Zoe saw a diamond so she followed him. He got away, but he left a diamond (he dropped it).

Zoe bent down and took the sparkling diamond.

"This could be from the crown," she thought. It certainly looked precious. Zoe went back to the poster. There was a phone number, so she rang it.

"Hello," said a low voice.

"Is this Buckingham Palace?" Zoe asked.

"Yes, it certainly is," the voice replied. "What do you want?"

"I think I may have found the thief of the Queen's crown,"

explained Zoe. "In my hand, I'm holding a diamond from the crown."

"Do you have any idea of what the thief looks like? Any details?" the low voice asked.

"He has a grey back-pack, and brown hair."

The phone went dead.

Within seconds, sirens and blue flashing lights swarmed the streets surrounding the bakery.

Within minutes, Zoe was surrounded.

"Hop in!" commanded an officer. "We need your vision."

Zoe did as she was asked, and away they sped.

"STOP!" shouted Zoe moments later.

She had seen the thief jump into a bus, but the bus was no match for speedy police cars. They had him cornered.

The thief was arrested, and the crown was returned to its rightful owner. Zoe received the reward of f270000, and, of course, became really popular. Not that she cared about being popular, but at least she had more than one friend. She wasn't embarrassed to wear her glasses any longer, and she didn't care what anybody thought of her.

Insect Glasses

By Joseph Naisbitt at St Joseph's Primary School

This is Tim. He is a young fly. He is a fly that lives in a minute house inside a bigger one, a human's house. Tim doesn't understand what humans exactly are, but he is not your average fly that lives in your modern house. He is a fly that hates his way of seeing. It is really hard to see with it!

He kept complaining, but then he finally got a reply. He didn't know what he needed or what it was!

A few moments later, Tim was looking up pictures of glasses.

"I really hate my way of seeing! There is just hexagons everywhere!" Tim complained.

"Tim, you are born with that way of seeing. If you really want to change it, you'll have to get some extremely small glasses! Be aware of that hostile human though," his mother replied.

Humans are a species that are very mean to insects. They are always armed with fly swatters –very deadly-- and are a very bad species to flies.

Then Tim flew off. He left the house and dodged the hostile human's swatter, then evaded some quicker cars thanks to his immeasurably crazy flight that he is getting used to.

"That was close," Tim said, like he got really close to the cars.

Finally, he made it to the opticians. But the automatic door wasn't working for him as he was as small as an ant. That can be a great advantage though- he flew through the gap and flew inside.

"Hello, can I have some really small glasses please? If you have some?" Tim asked.

But the receptionist did not notice. Tim's voice was too small to be heard!

"Excuse me, can you hear me?" Tim excused.

But the receptionist did not notice again! He was too busy helping another customer.

"Fine, I guess I'll find another optician, they'll be better than you!" Tim complained.

Then he flew away to find another optician. He flew past the speeding cars and trucks only to find another optician. He remembered what to do and what to ask, even though he had the mind of an old man.

However, it was about to close down. But that didn't stop him, so he flew inside.

But it wasn't what he expected. The receptionist noticed him, but he was armed with a fly swatter! Very dead fly Tim!

He luckily evaded the aggressive receptionist.

"I knew that was going to happen, stupid receptionist," Tim complained.

He decided to give up on today's lazy search and flew home – long travel. On the way, a tiny newspaper flew in his face.

It read:

THE INSECT TIMES
New insect optician opening today!
Any insect that buys gets in free today!
Come and book appointments for glasses now!

Come to 19 Grasshopper Street, DH1 94C, Durham.

"Oh boy! I finally get my glasses today! All I have to do is go to the address!" Tim rejoiced. So he flew, but the journey felt way safer. No cars, just a fly in the streets.

Finally, he flew to the optician he was looking for (insect optician). He got his eyes tested and got new glasses, 2, golden 3D glasses and flew all the way home.

"Mum, mum! I got the glasses!" Tim bragged to his mum.

"Tim, I'm proud of you sweetie. Maybe I should get my glasses sometime. I'm starting to dislike my way of seeing," his mother replied.

And so that was it. Tim's big mum went out to get some glasses, and Tim grew up to be a big fly. He married a butterfly called Reta – she was a pretty one.

And they lived happily ever after.

Only Hope

By Brandon Bartosiak at Trinity School

Year 1998, the day I was born, and my father was in the army but he can't make it home. My mother was a teacher. Life was hard for me when I felt scared without seeing and lost in the darkness.

I was only 5 when I lost my sight of a disease named "AMD".

My mother took me to the hospital to see a specialist. When the nurse called me into the doctor office, my mother told the specialist what's wrong. After the specialist asked me questions, after they took samples of blood and looked at my eye. When they were done taking samples to send to the research department and make me and my mother wait until the news was come.

I was waiting over 4 hours for news from the research department. When I hear my name called I get up with my mother leading me, but there was something I felt... like there's something wrong. We come back to the first room but I just got out of it. The nurse knocks on the door 3 times when a voice from the office saying "entry" the nurse opens the door.

Me and my mum went in and sat down and listened to the specialist.

The specialist told my mother: "the research department can't find anything to help, but the only way to fix the problem is to wait when the research department found a cure but I'm sorry for bad news ma'am."

My mother starts to cry and saying "I so sorry" and went up to hug me. I tried to cry but it's too hard to cry.

Me and my mother went home and wait for news from the research department but my mother "doesn't know when we going get news from them, my darling son."

The next morning at 9:23 am there was a mail from the research department. I grab the mail and get my mother in the sitting room and I say to my mother "here, a mail for you and me from the research department" my mother open the mail and read it.

Dear: ma'am Rose and Ben.

We figure out what wrong with your son Ben, there was a really bad eye disease Named Age Musher Disease, broke Ben's eye cell and make him blind. But there good news too, we figure a cure for your son Ben. It can help the pain and let Ben see clearly.

We will send the cure to you soon.

From: Research department.

My mother was so happy and for sometime cried on the table. I go to my mother and give her a hug.

Anonymous Opticians Strike Again

By Ofe at St Joseph's Primary School

It was 10:45 am, and the Anonymous Opticians, who were the most unsuccessful superheroes in the universe, were watching Mr. Sight's pet factor.

"Go on Lady poodles!" Craig chanted noisily.

"Noodles you can do it!" hoped Jake.

" Why are we still friends with those weirdos? " questioned Liv.

"I just don't know it's probably because we get to use cool inventions," answered Beth sarcastically.

" No. It's because were the coolest people in the world," replied Jake, full of himself.

" As-if! " said Liv knowing they weren't.

"Wait I can hear the dangerous, alerting alert button. It's Doctor Cry Face!" panicked Craig terrified.

Dr. Cry Face. A wicked mastermind, he was so evil he could do anything and get away with it. He was almost like a ghost. They picked the call and he started to talk with his sinister, deep, criminal voice.

"Welcome idiots. It's time for you to hear the most evil, unsolvable plan in the whole world. I'm going to erupt the deadly, daring and dangerous volcano of lost vision. For the next 1000 years, which will be eye hell, nobody will be able to see. P.S. you won't be able to solve that crime... you're way too stupid," he cackled.

"How awfully rude. I can't wait to prove him wrong," replied Jake annoyed.

Liv persuaded. "We need to solve that crime. For the poor, helpless people of Eyelank."

"People are in trouble, we need to save them. **HURRY!**" nagged Beth loudly.

***

When they got there Jake announced like a wimp, "Here it is, the place others call Eye Death."

"Don't over- exaggerate. If we don't make it at least we tried," doubted Liv.

"You're being silly. We're not going to die, are we?" pondered Craig worriedly.

Soon they entered the giant path to torture, wondering if they should go back or not.

Although the three hours went past, they finally entered the dark, gloomy **FESTIVAL** of colour and saw all kinds of mysteriously odd stuff- who knows where that came from? Branches the colour of coffee it was disgusting, and the amber scorching sun that felt like they were in a baked oven. And obviously demon crimson devil eyes, known for **biting people's heads off**, and having a passion for juicy, succulent, fresh **eyes**!

They were coming to hunt them down. They had to get to safety but it was **TOO LATE**! Soon later they were surrounded by the the creatures they assumed were cruel.

"What do you want? Money, food, sweets we've got it all," offered Jake.

"We've got a passion for eyes, but we're on a diet," said Master

Eye. Master Eye seemed to be the oldest there. He had a grey beard and glasses as dark as ink. At first, he looked very serious but then he loosened up.

The devil eyes decided they would give them half an hour then they warned if the job had not be done they would feed on their fresh, young skin.

They soon left and pondered were they were going to get the odd ingredient. They came across a sort of powder the colour of clay. They soon created a big blob that looked like a **slug's breakfast**!

"We're dead," said Beth, trying trying to keep hope, but failing terribly. They presented the disgusting blob sacredly. They looked at it like it was garbage passing it to each other in disgust trying to justify what it was. They agreed for their effort they can pass as long as they never stood foot there again. They four teenagers passed not looking back because they were just too scared.

After a few minutes, the curious four brave teenagers were ready to risk their eyesight and set off to the jungle of eye destruction home to the volcano of lost vision.

As they came further, they could hear a loud roaring noise it was like a volcano erupting from tigers, But in the distance you could see millions of tiger dens, what could it be...

They could hear footsteps behind them. Suddenly, Jake could sense a claw on his foot.

He felt aghast, confused.

"Who are you? Wait, have you seen my son he's been gone for months now," the tiger said curiously. "Can you help me?" she asked politely.

The brave four huddled in a group. After a while, they decided to help the poor tiger.

"See the problem is I can't reach the tree of luminous eyes. It's how me and my son communicate. If he sees them it will bring him right back to me," she said.

"If anyone is going to do it it's Jake. He's the best climber," mentioned Liv.

Soon, he swung from tree to tree like a natural, But he finally got it.

"I've got it," he announced celebrating. When he finally came down the woman eagerly got it and waved it in the air. Her son came running back to her they were a united family again.

As they approached further, it started to get scorching hot. They started to hear a booming, bubbling noise. At last it was the volcano of doom and lost vision. The moment of terror they've been waiting for.

"What if we never make it? What if we can't find a way to off it? I'm too young to die this was a bad idea," Listed Craig negatively.

"We're not going back we've came too far," convinced Liv.

For the next hour, they looked for the button. Urgently Beth spotted it. There it is you can off it," said Beth scared to Jake.

"You off it," said Jake.

"No. You off it," they argued.

"I'll off it. This is it," agreed Craig mortified. Then with caution, he pressed the dangerous button. The brave, four souls walked out knowing they were heroes.

A few weeks later, their news was universal newspapers, shop windows and TV news- even more. They soon got awarded by the queen of Eyelank - it was amazing. Now everyone respects them. Plus they were awarded 200,000 million pounds. And guess what? They used it to buy not only the best but newest laser eye 5000 that they used to get revenge on Dr. Cry Face.

And they bought with the rest of the money an optician which was the most successful thing yet. Finally they were good at something.

Smart Glasses

By Jessica at Belmont Community School

"Okay, try them on."

Natalia picked up the black glasses and put them on, only expecting her vision to improve, nothing else. And it did, nothing was blurry, however she also saw... something else. Red writing printed above the optician's head.

Dr. Chris Beck
Age: 38
D.o.B: 4/2/80
More...

Quickly she took them off and compared what she saw to reality. The writing was gone and everything was blurry again. Confused but needing to find out more, she paid and left.

As soon as she left the building, she put on the glasses in the busy streets, slightly worried about what she would see. Suddenly, her vision was clouded by more red writing. Information about everybody in the street printed up in front of her and she couldn't see anything for all the words in front of her.

"Watch it," someone told her in an annoyed tone. The words above her head said 'Jenny Smith'.

She muttered the name under her breath as she walked away

"What?" She heard her call out after her, but Natalia was already engulfed by the crowd of people to be seen.

When she finally arrived home she dared to try them on again and walked towards her sister.

Kia Anderson.
Age: 15
D.o.B: 3/1/04
More...

She wondered how to access more, but is what it contains really something she wanted to know? She felt the side of the glasses, looking for any sort of button. As she pressed something on the side, a a whole paragraph printed in front of her, about... everything.

Part 3:
Special Mentions

We received so many amazing stories that it was nearly impossible to narrow them down! So, just because a story didn't make the top 25 doesn't mean it wasn't amazing. And so, here are the rest, each and every one of them oozing with imagination and heart.

The Birdies of Silly Bird Forest

By Prince and Jocelyn at St Joseph's Primary school

Silly bird forest is a forest that lives with lots of splendid birds with beautiful feathers. Well, not all of them. The adult birdies are Transparent, Rainbow, Purple, Pink, Black, Bossy (Golden) and Wise. The little ones include Red, Orange, Splendid, Super and Same.

When Same was born, Transparent was so excited and he said "another transparent birdie! Same as me! Let's call him Same." Same is also Transparent. Purple, Pink, Black, and Bossy(Golden) have feathers just like their names show. Red and Orange are twins. Red is a boy and Orange is a girl.

The kid birdies go to Silly Bird School.

One clear night all the birdies fly again to the tallest tree in silly bird forest to watch the stars as usual. This is always their favourite before bed activity. The big Dipper shines brightly in the dark night. Red, Orange, Splendid and Super are so excited. Super said "I spotted the Big Dipper first today!".

"No, me, me..." said the others. They just couldn't quiet down.

Then, Same wondered why he didn't spot any star tonight. It was just a cloudy night for him. He asked "did you really see the stars, guys?", but their friends were busying fighting for who was the first one to have spotted the big dipper and didn't hear him at all.

After star-watching the kids birdies raced back to their home. Same tried to follow them, but he found it was foggy everywhere and he bumped into the trees sometimes on his way home. Then, he thought reading his favourite books might cheer himself up. After all, for a super bookworm like him, reading always made him happy. However, when he tried to read, he found all the words on every page blurred and he couldn't see them clearly. Finally, he fell asleep miserably.

The next day, Same woke up late and didn't want to go out to play. He stayed at home all day long. When evening came, his friends became worried about him as they didn't see him a whole day. Then, they came to check whether everything was OK with Same.

"Are you OK, Same?" asked Splendid.

"Why not come to play today?" said Red.

"No, I'm not feeling well. I think there is something with my eyes. Everything is vague around me. I can't even read my books," answered Same.

"Oh, sorry Same. But we can't check your eyes, you are invisible and we can't see you," said Super.

"Maybe we can ask the adult birdies for help," said Orange.

Then, Red and Orange went and told all the adult birdies to come. Later on Rainbow, Transparent, Pink, Golden and Black all came. However, after a heated discussion, they still had no clue what had happened to Same.

"Maybe it's time to turn to Wise for help. He seems to know everything," said Same in a tiny and weak voice.

Wise is an owl living in Silly Bird Forest. As the name suggested, he is the wisest bird in this forest.

"Yes! Yes!" Everyone agreed.

Red and Orange went to Owl's home and told him everything. Ten, Wise came with something strange in his hand. He asked Same to put this thing on his eyes.

"Oh! That's amazing! Everything is clear now! What a magic!" said Same excitedly.

Everybody saw this strange thing flying up and down with Same!

"Please tell us, what is this, Wise?" Asked everybody curiously.

"Glasses!" answered Wise. "And what's happened to Same's eyes is called near-sightedness. It is an eye disorder where light focuses in front of, instead of on, the retina. This causes objects to be blurry......"

Wise went on and on with everybody feeling more confused.

"Ok, sorry. I didn't mean to confuse you. What I mean is Same reads a lot in his home with weak light, so his eyes are sick and needs these glasses to help. And you need to protect your eyes in future and read in places with proper light. Same." said wise.

Same became a happy boy again with his glasses. He still reads a lot but not in the faint light.

Glass Girls

By Rosie at St Joseph's Primary School

Part 1: Before

"So, Violet. Which ones to you fancy?" he asked me.

Secretly, I didn't want any, but I didn't say it aloud. I looked at the glasses again, but again none caught my eye. I had just had my first eye test and the optician told my mum I needed glasses.

"Well," said mum, eyeing me, as if I had just said the weirdest thing in the world, "which ones?"

I looked at the glasses again and again, and suddenly I saw some pretty purple ones with multi coloured hearts on. I slowly raised my hand and pointed.

"Good choice!" said the optician, smiling. "I'll just make sure they fit..." He put them on my face and led me over to a mirror. The moment I saw them on my face, I knew they were perfect. They stood out from my flowing, brown hair and my bright, blue eyes shone through them like stars. A grin spread across my face reaching my ears.

"I guess that's a yes." he said, handing them to me.

Mum didn't need to remind me to say thank you as she usually did. I was so happy that I just said it straight away.

"Thank you!"

Part 2: The awful present

Now I was in a stuffy classroom and couldn't concentrate on what the teacher was saying. If she really meant it, then why hadn't she done it there and then? I have no idea? The bad news is, I also have no idea how I will survive my first day.

At break, I saw a girl standing in a corner. I considered going over but I couldn't summon the courage. I wandered round the playground and just then, I bumped into that girl again. The one who said she would do it. She was a bully. I hated her.

"You think your glasses are awesome. Don't you," she smirked.

"you think *you're* awesome for that matter!"

"Actually, I don't." I say confidently.

"Oh. Shall I just tell everyone even *you t*hink you're a stupid little worm."

"No," I squeaked, a little less confident.

"HA!" she shouted. A lot of kids looked our way. She glared at them and strutted off.

***

Next lesson was PE. PE is my favourite lesson (partly because it is the only one I like). As I did at my old school, when we were asked to find partners, I just waited for someone to be left so I was with them. Right now, the person who was left, was the girl who had been in the corner at break. We had to do backward rolls. I was quite happy because I like doing backward rolls. To my surprise, we both said exactly the same at exactly the same time...

"Do you want to go first?" Startled, the girl jumped.

"Are you okay? You look worried! Can you do a backward roll?"

"No, yes," she said.

"What's the matter then?"

"I have an eye test tonight. I'm nervous."

"It will be fine. I had an eye test about a week ago. I had to get glasses."

"I definitely don't want glasses!"

"I'm sure you won't need them," I said, trying to be comforting whilst thinking about the bully.

"You sure?"

"Yes," I say, "anyway let's get on with backward rolls shall we."

Part 3: My new friend

The next day, my new friend came back to school with *glasses*! I couldn't believe my eyes!

"Hello!" I say, eyes shining at not being the only one with glasses.

"Hi," she said, glumly. I stared at her but she just looked at me and sighed. I thought she was mad for a second but then I remembered her words she spoke yesterday....

"I definitely don't want glasses!" I looked at her and sighed.

"I'm sorry."

"It's fine! I was just joking you!"

"Ha, ha."

"We should have a gang. Give it a name."

"Like what?"

"Glass Girls!" she smiled.

"Okay!" just then, the bell rang.

Me and my new friend hurried inside but just before we entered the class I asked, "What's your name?"

"Lila," she replied. We stepped inside.

***

Dear diary,

today was totally awesome! I made a new friend and her name is Lila. I can't wait until tomorrow! Also today I managed to avoid that bully. For tea tonight, my mum is doing sausage and Yorkshire pudding. Yum yum! I wish every day could be like this one. I wish wishes could come true but obviously they don't.

Part 4: Super Glass

Today was Saturday. Not just any old Saturday! The day of the first meeting for Glass Girls! Me and Lila were meeting up in the park tonight next to the big willow. It's branches are so long they touch the bright, green grass and are so thick that it's impossible to see the trunk of the tree, It would make the ideal meeting place on a sunny Saturday morning.

***

I put on my clothes and I heard the TV giving out the morning news to anyone who would bother listening. I padded downstairs into the kitchen to see about breakfast. Who should I see but my dad on his I-pad listening to the radio.

"Dad!" I say, overjoyed because my dad works away so most of the time he's not here. He looked up.

"Violet!" A smile slowly spread across my dad's face. "I'm back for a whole week! Isn't that great!"

"It's awesome!"

I got some cereal and put it in a bowl. Suddenly, I heard my phone ring.

"Hello?" I said.

"It's Lila, Violet. How are you? Actually, where are you? I'm already at the willow!"

"I'm on my way now," I said, surprised.

"Hurry up!" she ended the call. I rushed to the bathroom, grabbed my tooth brush, and brushed my teeth. While I was doing this, mum passed the bathroom and I couldn't resist the urge to say,

"Dad's back!"

"I know!"

I suddenly remembered Lila and the gang.

"Got to go!" I say hurriedly, as I ran down the stairs.

"Bye," shouted mum, but she was too late. I was already running towards the front gate.

Part 5: Catastrophe

I arrived at the park at 9:23 and met Lila at the willow. I was exhausted from running and the sun beat on the back of my neck, causing beads of sweat to trickle down my back.

"What took you so long?" she grinned as if we were old friends. I stumbled inside the branches of the willow and slumped down against the trunk of the tree. I was grateful for the shade and cool of the den.

"Well?" she said, "What are we here to do?"

"Talk about the gang and maybe have a wander round the park."

"It's massive! We'll never get around all of it!"

"Who said we were going round all of it?" I laughed.

"Phew!" said Lila.

***

We chatted about our gang. We played hide and seek, tag, pretended to be explorers and before we knew it we were at our favourite place in the park... The maze!

"Whoa!" said Lila, taking it all in.

"I know right. It's amazing!"

"Let's go in!" Lila said eagerly.

"Okay but we neee...!" I couldn't finish. Lila was pulling me into the maze and running off!

"Wait!" I shouted frantically before taking off after her! I soon saw her heels disappear round a corner but by the time I got there she was nowhere to be seen. I had come... to a junction.

Part 6: Lost

Noooooo! I thought. *I've lost you!*

But then I stopped. I could see footprints on the floor. Slowly, I took my glasses off and looked exactly where the prints were. There were none. I put my glasses back on and I could see them again! My glasses are awesome! I started to follow my friend's tracks but almost immediately I got mixed up and followed other people's tracks to a dead end.

What was funny with this track though, was that it didn't lead back out of the dead end. It just stopped. It was like the person who they'd belonged to had just flown into the sky and away. But I couldn't do that with Lila just out there in the maze. Lost, I sat down on the wet, mossy grass. I started to cry. I couldn't help it. They just came trickling down my face like rain from the clouds. I fell asleep.

Part 7: Lila

"Violet, violet! Wake up!" I jolted awake. A figure stood over me. It was dark, all around me. One question stayed in my mind. Where was I?

"Where am I?" I croaked. I only just managed to get the words out.

"You're at a dead end, in a maze, at night." Then all my memories came back.

"Is that you Lila? I thought I'd lost you?"

"It's me and you'll never lose me. I'll always come looking for you, just like I did today. Though it took rather a long time."

I laughed but then I realized it was night.

"We have to get out of here!" I said frantically.

"Hold my hand and I'll guide you." said Lila calmly. In the dark

149

I reached for her hand and she led me out of the maze, into the cold night air and to safety.

Once we were out of the maze, it was easier to tell where we were going. We retraced our steps, this time not playing hide and seek, tag and pretending to be explorers. I shivered. It was cold walking in the night, and spooky too. All the sounds of nature seemed to be against you.

***

By the time we were out of the park I was glad. It didn't seem as spooky out here as in the park. But then we came to Lila's street.

"I have to go," she said, "This is my street."

"Bye," I said, and walked on. It was much spookier without Lila so I quickened my pace. Soon, I reached my street. It was a relief because the street lights were casting an eerie light onto the darkened pavement. I sprinted along my street until I reached number 13 and as quiet as possible stepped inside. It was welcoming to enter the warm house and see things I knew so well. I took off my shoes and crept up the stairs. One of the stairs creaked and I flinched but no one upstairs stirred so I continued. I reached the landing, tiptoed into my bedroom and slipped under the covers. I fell asleep.

Part 8: Bullies

Dear diary,

*yesterday night was <u>really</u> creepy. I need to tell you something I've never told anyone else before. Promise not to tell? OK. **I'm afraid of the dark.** Phew. That totally helps now that I've told you that. Now you can help me get through life when things are tough. Bye!*

***

I entered the playground that day intending to meet Lila at our usual meeting place but the bully came up to me,

"Here's the little brat again!"

"Oh no," I groaned, "Not you again! I just want you out of my life!"

"Oh yeah. Think about how I feel."

"Well if you stay out of my life I'll stay out of yours."

"Deal? **No thank you** I am *made* to be in people's lives."

"So am I!"

"Big deal."

"Hey," I shouted, offended.

"You just lost. Loser!"

"You're the loser *and* the bully," I muttered under my breath.

Part 9: Resolution

After school, I hung out in the park with Lila. A girl with glasses came past but we didn't think much of it at first. Then, I realized it was the bully!

"Oh!" I squealed.

"What?" asked Lila.

"Sarah. She's got glasses!"

"Let's go see!" We ran over.

"You've got glasses!" exclaimed Lila.

"So what?"

"Well, I guess that means you could join our gang," I looked questioningly at Lila.

"Yeah, why not?" said Lila, "It's called Glass Girls."

We chatted about our gang. We played hide and seek, tag and pretended to be explorers. We've been good friends ever since.

The end!

Simon Sneaks Out

By Jakey at St. Joseph's Primary School

One hot sunny day around about 6 o'clock in the morning, a little boy called Simon, who lived in a cottage, opened his curtains and got ready for school.

After a couple of minutes his mum woke up, and Simon asked "can I play with Ruffle, my dog?"

"Yes dear, but only for 5 minutes because we need to take you to the optician's to get your eyes tested," his mum said.

"B-but I don't like eye tests," he stammered and cried.

But he went to play with his dog.

"But what about school?" Simon asked.

"You're not going to school, you're going to the opticians," his mum told him after, time and time again.

Simon was only trying not to go to the optician's. He would do anything not to go to the optician's but I suppose he had to. Sneakily he went round the back gate and walked to the bus stop. When he got picked up from the bus stop to get to school he saw everyone wearing glasses. He thought he was dreaming but he wasn't.

Not long after he went to school his mum called to him and was going out to look for him. Simon had the key, so that was okay for him, but when his mum went out the house, Simon went in the house.

Simon shouted "Mum, Mum where are you I've been out playing with Ruffle!" He lied.

Soon as his mum stepped in the house she shouted "SIMON get down here right now!!!"

Simon knew he was going to be in trouble. "I'm taking you to the optician's right now, so come on!" his mum said angrily.

So when they got to the opticians he could read the top line, but not the bottom or any other line. The opticians said you need to wear glasses and he went off to look for a pair. Simon got a pair of Spiderman glasses. His mum said "you can wear these tomorrow at school. They will look good on you."

The next day he went to school with his Spiderman glasses and everyone laughed at him, so he told the teacher and the teacher didn't take any notice of him. So when he got home he told his mum and his mum took him back to the optician's and got him some plain black ones. His mum said "now no-one will laugh at you, don't you worry."

The next day he went to school he was a bit worried that everyone would laugh at him. But then he got to the school gates everyone started playing with him and he thought he looked like everyone else so that was good.

Vision dog

By Sophie Lye at St Joseph's Primary School

It was a Sunday, sunny and bright. Everyone was cheerful and busy but there was one person who was not in the mood. His name was Mikey and he was an old man who would never(ever) have a smile on his face. As he was walking down the path, everyone was smiling at him and trying to cheer him up. It wouldn't work though, the Grinch is what people used to call him because he would never smile and he would spoil parties. Mikey was coming to the road when he saw one of his friends. The only time you would see him smiling was with his friends. While he crossed the road, he waved to his friend when all of a sudden a deafening sound came out of nowhere...

It was Mikey screaming "HELP!" there had been a car crash and Mikey was in it. Everyone gathered around him panicking and not knowing what to do. Mikey was hit at the back of his head but his eyesight went really blurry. He couldn't see anything because there was so many people around him. It was frightening. All Mikey had to do was sit there and hope some rang for help.

After all the drama that had happened and everyone panicking Mikey finally arrived at the hospital in a quiet room. Everything was really blurry like it was at the accident. Next to him was a pair of glasses.

"Wow," he thought. Mike looked at them and hesitated. Then all of a sudden a miracle happened, Mikey could see again!

Out of nowhere skidding came across the floor. A golden face; silly and jolly, panting away was a dog! This dog was no ordinary dog. He was a guide dog for Mikey to look after because of his eyesight! Mikey would now have someone in his house and he might not be as moody anymore. Mikey and his dog(Max) had so much fun together and Mikey's eyesight was getting better and better because of his glasses. He had to go to the opticians more though. He was finally a happy and jolly man.

Flame Glasses

By Asia at St Joseph's primary school

Hi, my name is Calypso and I am 16 years old with a lot more adventures than lives. In my life I have had at least 50 near-death moments but I'm still here! This is the story of how I became immortal and got 10 kids.

My father sent me on a mission to find the Throne of Fire. The Throne of Fire was in an Egyptian desert but I didn't entirely know how to get there. As I was walking along heated sand, I found a mummy. It was covered in sand but it was clearly extremely old. Away from the oasis, I started dragging this repulsive thing, The oasis was filled with fruit, water, green grass and a peculiar water tank. Walking towards the water tank, I put the mummy down but I didn't see the sign that said "BEWARE! QUICKSAND!" As I started sinking through very fast, I didn't have time to close my eyes. Suddenly, I realised that my legs had touched solid floor!

Without hesitation, the mummy started moving and pulling me through an opening. To me it looked blurry so I just went with the flow. The sand must have got into my eyes and scratched them! For a split second I thought I had gone blind because I saw such a light that I didn't know what it was, The mummy had taken me to a room filled with more grotesque mummies. They picked me up and sat me on a chair made out of sandstone – to get an eye test. As I had some sand in my eyes, I couldn't close them so it was easy to have a test. They used an unusual stick thing to get all the sand out of my eyes which made it a lot better. Ra (the god of the Sun) told me that I have to have glasses! Glasses gave me butterflies in my tummy but I was OK with them. Ra made me some glasses out of fire but didn't give me them because he didn't know if I was going to burn.

It took us an endless time to get to the throne of Fire because it was through a lot of passages and tunnels. Once we finally got there, I opened my bag to take out the Orb of Fire but the sand under me formed a slope and I was pushed towards the fire. Sadly, I couldn't see properly so I just let myself slide down. Thankfully, I was fire immune so the fire didn't do anything to me therefore Ra gave me the glasses.

Once we got out of the hole, Ra gave me the power to be the Goddess of the sun and marry him. Now I am immortal with 10 kids all with glasses. Their names are: Sadie, Carter, Lucy, Karla, Wendy, Walt, Natsu, Ursa, Mirra-Jane, Jellal. Sadie, Carter and Walt are triplets; Lucy and Karla are twins; Wendy and Mirra-Jane are twins;

Ursa and Jellal are twins; Natsu is just alone.

The orphan and her mysterious glasses

By Dionne at St. Joseph's

In a populated orphanage, there lives a kind and caring girl called Amy. She had blond hair and blue eyes. Amy sadly has to put up with the awful orphanage though. You're not allowed any toys or pets! The lady who owns this awful orphanage is called Mrs Modey.

Amy has a pet but nobody knows about it. Amy has a dog called Angel. Angel doesn't live in the orphanage. Angel is a stray with brown eyes and black and white fur. Angel is 5 years old and Amy is 12 which is 7 years older than Angel.

On one ordinary day Amy was just sleeping in her blue and red stripy bed. Somebody knocked on the door. Amy ignored them. Then came another loud knock. Amy got out of her warm and cosy bed and she had a massive, tired yawn. She stumbled towards the door and she opened it.

"Morning," Amy said in a tired voice.

"Good morning Amy, it's nice to see you!" said Mrs Modey in a very joyful voice.

Why is she so happy to see me? Amy asked herself. *She hates me!*

Amy looked to the right and saw a man in a smart tuxedo and black, silky trousers. He was wearing black, dull sunglasses. To the side of the man standing tall was a lady in a bright, blue, and beautiful dress.

The secretive man asked Amy some questions like "what's your name?" and "how old are you?"

Amy answered the questions truthfully. After that the man revealed his name.

"I'm Jordan and I'm 32 years old. I have to go for, erm, stuff."

"Bye!" said the lady in the bright, blue, beautiful dress.

They both left except for Mrs Modey. Mrs Modey went over to Amy and whispered "Mr. Jordan and Mrs. Emily (Jordan's wife) Seem interested in you. They might adopt you..."

Mrs Modey left the room.

Amy sat on her bed puzzled. "Will I be adopted? I don't know if I want to be!"

Angel came stealthily to see Amy. Angel scratched at the door, Amy opened the door. Angel barked twice, then she darted out of the door as fast as a leopard. Amy charged after her.

"Owww," Amy said, as she bumped into Mr. Jordan.

She secretly picked up angel and went upstairs. After lots of play with Angel, Angel left. Amy went to get her colouring book out of her bag and she found these magical looking glasses. She put them on and she had powers!

Amy heard a loud and worried dog cry. It was Angel's. Amy looked out of her window and she saw a building on fire! Angel was inside!

She flew over to the burning house and saved angel. Amy hugged her tight. There wasn't a single burn on either of them.

***

Then Jordan looks in his bag for his glasses. "Oh no!" he yells. He found a colouring book. Jordan's and Amy's bags were switched! They look the same! Jordan luckily has a tracking device on his bag so he started to track Amy!

Jordan found Amy after many clues. "I'm an agent," Jordan whispered to Amy.

"Cool!" she replied.

"You can keep the glasses." Jordan whispered. "Also, I'm adopting you and your dog."

"Yay!" Amy screamed.

Amy, Angel and Mr. Jordan went home and live happily ever after.

The end

Simon's eye test

By Phoebe at St. Joseph's Primary School

There was once a brother and sister that go by the names of Delia and Simon. Simon would usually play videogames in his room whilst Delia was baking your favourite foods.

One day, whilst Simon was playing videogames, everything started to go blurry and he couldn't see very well. He decided to forget about it and go to school the next day, until this happened. Everything had gone blurry and he couldn't see or do his work so he told his friend, clover. Delia had caught him talking so she told the teacher. He tried to deny it and say he was fine... but he was standing at the opposite side of the room.

Delia pulled him over and said that she had caught him talking. The teacher called parents and they immediately booked an appointment for Simon.

In the car, Delia tried to make conversation about the fact that if Simon had gone blind and needed glasses then he couldn't do basketball. They don't accept players with glasses on the team for some reason. When they arrived, Simon started to ask lots of strange questions like "how do you milk a cow?" or "are you homeless?"

There were no answers. He came back home with glasses whilst a tiny puppy was sitting on his bed just for him. At home, Simon went out to play with his puppy and show off to his friends whilst Delia was trying to fix her burnt muffins. His parents had arrived with him as they caught him driving back home, so he had gotten grounded but in the end, they were all just watching TV eating some delicious popcorn.

Norman's Journey

By Owen at St. Joseph's Primary School

June 1939

Dear Diary,

It started as an ordinary day, getting up from my bed which is as soft as sheep wool. Opened the blackout curtains and gazed at the beautifully pink sky. My jaw dropped at the sight. When I looked down, London disintegrated (it looked like it had been put through a shredder!)

Clearing the lump in my throat, I called mam to report the monstrosity. No answer. Second time, no answer. Filled with fright, I decided to tiptoe downstairs. Finally, I reached the kitchen- she wasn't there. Wandering in, I scanned the kitchen, to find a note which read 'got to go darling, suitcase is packed for evacuation'.

WHAT.

I couldn't believe it...

Norman

***

June 1939

Dear diary,

Dear diary, a rollercoaster day went on yesterday. I'll give you a quick catch-up. After the monstrosity that happened on Monday, I had to run to the station which is 30 minutes away. The only problem is, my train is in 15 minutes. Sprinting as quick as a flash, I ran half with ease. Then my legs stopped dead. I wasn't going to make it!

Thankfully, Mac (and his psychic powers) were driving by when I was blue. In the end, I caught my train, however I hadn't caught my GLASSES!

Norman

***

July 1939

Dear Diary,

I hate life here. First of all, I am nicknamed stinky winky. Also, there is a permanent smell of manure. Even if I'm by myself, I want to be in London.

Norman

***

July 1939

Dear diary,

Life has flicked a switch. John, my 'owner' has walked me to Simon Berry's. If you don't know, he is an optician. So now I have glasses- it feels like coming back from the dead.

A true story of Amy and Adam

By Amy at Durham Blue Coat school

This story is about me and my brother. It all started when Adam was 18 months old, he got his eyes tested at the hospital and they found out that he had a squint. He had to go choose some glasses that he liked and he felt all different because he had never had an experience with glasses before.

At school when I was 5 I had my eyes tested and they found out that I was long sighted. It felt like there was nothing worse because I didn't want to wear glasses. I chose some purple ones and then when I got to school they helped me to read better and look at screens for longer. I knew that I could get used to the new glasses and now as you are reading this I am very grateful for what my glasses have done to help me.

Me and Adam go to Simon Berry's for new glasses and to get our eyes tested. We really like going because they have a good range of glasses and always something that suits you, and they have friendly staff.

In the room where we get our eyes tested we have to tell the person who is testing if there are any problems. We have to say the letters we can see on the board with one eye covered with tape. There are big letters and as they go down the board they get smaller. We also get a photo of our eyes and they can see in that photo if there is any damage or not.

Now I am 9 and Adam is 7 and we are very happy with our glasses all thanks to Simon Berry.

A Good Day

By Zara Carr at Trinity School

She was at her home. She was sitting in her chair but she couldn't see anything. She went to her first eye test but she was worried. But when the worker told her her to not worry she calmed down but she got her first pair of glasses but they were red and green. She was happy and excited that she got her first glasses but she went to bed and she put her first pair of glasses she put them in her glasses case.

When she woke up she put her glasses on and had her breakfast and it was good and had apricot orange juice and polished her glasses. They were mucky so she polished glasses and they was shiny again and put them back on, went to the bus and went to the shops and bought her groceries and went back on the bus and went back home to put her shopping away. Then she ate her dinner and it was good job and then she was washing up. Then she had a nap and relaxed for two hours and had chips and nuggets and it was good.

And she put her glasses in the glasses case and went to bed and snored and snored and snored and slept and had a good time.

Glasses or not?

By Kirsty at Trinity School

All her life Alice has worn her pink glasses, she got them when she was five and has loved them growing up. When Alice started school she made lots of friends and they all loved her pink glasses. When Alice turned fourteen she started big school, she was very nervous about what people would think of her. Would they like her? Would they hate her? Would she make friends? Or would she feel empty?

Happily Alice made friends with a group of girls.

"What is in that little bag on your arm?" one of the girls asked.

"Nothing," Alice quickly said, putting the bag in her backpack.

The reason she didn't want her new friends to know about her glasses was because she thought they wouldn't like her anymore and they would call her ugly.

Later in the day Alice went to the toilet since her eyes were hurting from not wearing her glasses, she couldn't see the questions on her test in maths or see the words I the book they were reading in English. As she washed her face she saw she couldn't see herself in the mirror, so she pulled her glasses onto her eyes. Seeing she could see everything clearly, she smiled then she was about to leave when one of her friends walked in.

Her eyes widened in shock; there was no way she could explain this to her.

Her friend stared confused.

Alice felt like a spider that had been spotted by a human.

"Why are you wearing glasses for?" she asked.

Alice took a deep breath, closing her eyes. "I have to wear these glasses because they help me see things well."

Her friend looked more confused. "But you weren't wearing glasses before!"

"I didn't wear them before because I was scared you would think I was ugly and wouldn't be my friend anymore."

Alice looked down until she felt a hand on her shoulder. As she looked up she met her friend's eyes.

176

"I don't care that you wear glasses and your true friends shouldn't either."

From then on Alice wore her glasses with confidence. After school she went on to be a writer and she wrote about her story and told people all over the world if you wear glasses you shouldn't hide, embrace it.

Super Girl Savannah's new glasses

By St. Hildes Nursery Class

Savannah was running around the park. Her glasses fell off and landed on the metal floor. Some naughty boys threw her glasses into the tree. They broke in two! Savannah started to cry.

She went to the optician's to get some new glasses. She picked the Super Girl glasses and turned into Super Girl Savannah! She flew back to the park and picked up those naughty boys and put them into jail, so they couldn't break any more glasses.

Super Girl Tilly's new glasses

By St. Hildes Nursery Class

Super Girl Tilly woke up on Monday 18th march at 7 o'clock. She brushed her teeth, dressed up in her clothes and went to school to save people. But on the way to school she pulled her glasses and SNAP! They broke!

Super girl Tilly started to cry. Mammy took her to the opticians. She went in and ran to the glasses. She picked the superhero unicorn glasses. She loved them. She walked back to school to show her friends her new glasses. Tilly was happy. Her friends loved her new glasses. They all wanted glasses just like her.

Ivy's X-ray Glasses!

By Eve at St. Joseph's Primary School

Hi my name is Ivy, and I have blondy brown hair and it's always in a plait or two, I also have blue eyes and am 10 years old. I live with my mam, my dad, and little brother Oscar. He has blonde hair and light green eyes, also he is 7 years old. My life is ok the only bad thing is I am doing something I have never done before... getting my EYES TESTED!

No-one in my class (which is the craziest class in school) has glasses and I need to keep it that way.

Got to go to school now, bye!

THE NEXT DAY

Today was the day I was going to get my eyes tested. When I was at the opticians. The person who tested my eyes said "you NEED GLASSES!"

I begged not to get glasses. I said "what if I get bullied?"

My mam said "I don't think so."

I had to stay at the opticians while my mam had to go pick up Oscar (who is annoying) from school. After 10 minutes my mam saw me in my new glasses which were blue on one side and and green on the other and a greeny blue colour in the middle.

I said sadly "let's just go but I'm sitting in-..."

"SHOTGUN," my brother said quickly.

I ran to the car and sat in the front. "Ha!" I said while laughing.

MONDAY

This morning my glasses kept falling off.

"Uhhh," I said to myself. "They're too BIG uhhhh," I shout.

"Oscar come downstairs let me do your hair," my dad shouted so the whole house can hear.

Oscar screamed "HAIR!"

"Oscar we are going to school now bye!" mam screamed upstairs.

MIDDAY MONDAY

I got to school and felt like an unuseful thing because I was wearing glasses. I asked my BFF's sister Lily if she was here.

Lily said "no."

"Ok," I said quietly.

Suddenly a group of girls came and said "NERD! BLIND PERSON!"

The person who said that was wearing a dark blue t-shirt and her hair was mouse brown which was tied back in a high ponytail, she was wearing that because it was non-uniform day.

MONDAY NIGHT

If you didn't know my mam and dad are scientists, but I have been keeping something secret ever since I got glasses.... I have **X-RAY** vision!

So I can help mam and dad maybe... NAH...

Got to go to tea now bye.

Guess what? I caught my brother reading my diary.

"Y... Y... You have **X-RAY VISION**?"says my brother.

"Yeah, I do," I said quietly waiting for an answer, but I didn't get one.

Good night.

***

I told my mam I got bullied yesterday.

"Come on, we will talk about it in the car sweetie," said Mam.

"Yey! Something cool to talk about in the car," Oscar said happily.

Dad said "No, you're going in my car... need to talk about having year 5 and 6 as friends."

"HA!" I said cheekily.

6 hours later I am back from school now and you probably

know what happened. Got bullied **AGAIN.**

***

It's been a week since I've written in this diary, but on the weekend I went with my mam and dad to work to try help them make a potion and I did. Since I have X-ray vision I can see through anything. I made potion, they are trying it out next week.

WAIT!

I've just found some small writing on the side of my glasses. It says **X-RAY** in blue!

1 week later we just finished testing my potion and it WORKS!

Today is the day when I am getting my reward. What shall I wear? Emmmm.... My white dress.

I just found out my brother is coming, he's wearing a black suit.

What is my reward?

My mam and dad are wearing their science kit.

"Okay I'm there," I thought to myself. "What do I do now?"

After 10 minutes, I was on stage, everyone clapping. My reward was here. It's a mini science kit for me and a science book.

"THANKS!" I say.

It was the BEST DAY EVER!

Laser Glasses

By Jackie at St Joseph's Primary School

Once there was a young boy called Jackie. He was incredibly popular and respected, until he got glasses. When he first got glasses all of his friends left him and he found himself being bullied everyday. He became as lonely as a picture on a wall.

But one day he was sitting in his room bored to death, and he was fidgeting with his glasses. Then he spotted a weird button which was hidden on the side of his glasses. He was very unsure of what the button did so he clicked the button, and then lasers shot out the lenses of the glasses.

Jackie thought to himself, I must never tell a soul about this because everyone will come to me wanting to be my friend and I will get bullied and I will say "NO!"

The next day a bully (in a ripped jacket) went to him and they started to call him names and they beat him up.

Then Jackie went up to the bully and burned him with his laser glasses.

After Jackie got the bully everyone wanted to be his friend. Jackie said "I will be none of your friends, because you only want to be my friend because of my laser glasses."

All of the bullies wanted to get their hands on Jackie because of when he attacked the bully with his lasers.

The next day all of the bullies went up to Jackie and started to call him names, and they also beat him up. Jackie was getting sick of all the bullies. Jackie had to get rid of his glasses and swap them for contact lenses due to the bullying.

Savannah's First Test

By Nicole Kirkley at St. Joseph's Primary School

Hello everybody, my name is Savannah.

I am five years old.

My mam woke me up one day to tell me something; I was exploding with excitement to see what it was she was going to tell me. But my excitement changed to worry when mam said to me "I don't think you are going to like it."

"I am sure I will," I replied.

"You are probably not going to be over impressed about it but you are going to go and get your eyes tested."

I replied "WHAT!? I don't want to go," but mam promised me it would be fun. Apparently the gigantic machines were extraordinary!

Also I might get a lolly when I go.

I eventually said "I will go but just for the lolly."

***

It was the next day(the horrible next day). My appointment was 11 o'clock. Mum told me what they would do to me. That made me even more worried. Mam said they would sit me on a chair, which was a very cool moveable chair, and turn the lights off. I was thinking in my head no, because I don't like the dark.

Mum said "it won't be that dark, anyways they will put funny glasses on you, then it will be the big big decision."

I had a second thought; Mum has glasses but still I wouldn't like them myself.

Mum said "don't feel like that, I think glasses are really cool."

I thought um... opposite.

***

My experience began when we got there (finally). My mam had to fill in some forms. My mam told me my cool, savage optician was called Laura. This is the same one my mam has – super nice.

But then she called me in and my mood changed a lot. I sat in

189

the cool, moveable chair. Then she turned the light off and that scared me. I had to read letters but what I didn't understand was that I couldn't read all the letters on the wall. Then Laura turned all of the lights on again.

"Bad news," announced Laura. "You are losing sight in your left eye."

Now I was WORRIED!

***

The next morning I went downstairs for my breakfast. Mam wanted to talk to me (again).

She said "when I was your age I had glasses and still do, and everyone thought they were really cool, even grandma!"

I replied "well in my opinion I would describe cool as the last word for glasses."

But then I had a second thought. If I got pink (magical) unicorn ones it would be amazing!

Mum said "well I don't think there would be any problem with that!"

From that moment on I was happy.

***

Two weeks later it was time for my next appointment. This time I was (super) excited. Not the slightest bit worried. Actually, I was hoping they would say I needed glasses. Later on that day it was actually time.

We got there really quick this time because we had to take the car seeing as it was raining. We finally got there. Mum filled out some forms again. Then I was called in by Laura.

She said "I know you won't like this but the results of your tests have come back negative so you are going to have to get glasses."

I replied excitedly "that's so good but only if you have got pink (magical) unicorn glittery ones!"

Laura replied, "yes I have them right here for you your mum told me what you wanted all I have to do now is test your size for your glasses.

I said "ok that's fine, I am super excited!"

Laura said "they are perfect! That means you can take them home today!"

I replied "thank you so much!"

I agreed after that that maybe glasses were cool, and so did mam.

Patricia

By Gabriella at St Joseph's Primary School

This is Patricia.

Her favourite colour is pink, and she loves animals(especially cats!). She has long brown hair and a goofy smile. She sounds pretty normal to you doesn't she? Well... she can't see as well as other people(she wasn't that popular as well). For the past few days she has been bullied. Manipulated all because she couldn't see (also because she was bumping into things).

Patricia started not wanting to go to school. She felt worthless.

Unaccompanied.

Invisible.

But little did Patricia know that her life was going to change!

Just by going to the opticians and getting her eyes tested for the first time ever.

Later that day when Patricia arrived at her house, she came to her Mam with tears running down her face.

"Are you ok Patricia? Has anything happened at school?" asked Patricia's Mam, who was wearing a white T-shirt, with a sweet and soft voice.

"Uh Mam, people are making fun of me! I think I need to go and get my eyes tested, Mam," said Patricia sobbing.

A few minutes later, her mam got on the phone to the opticians. Her mam called from downstairs, "Patricia! Your appointment to get your eyes tested is tomorrow, Ok?!"

"Ok and thanks Mam!" Patricia replied from her room, while fixing her face from when she was crying.

***

It was the next day, Patricia is going to get her eyes tested. She had just arrived at the opticians.

"Welcome! Your appointment is now, Patricia, your eye doctor is in room 4," the cheery, happy receptionist said in a joyful voice. Patricia was nervous and scared because it was her first time getting her eyes tested. Next she overheard the eye doctor say to her mam that she needed glasses. She got shocked, excited and sad at the same time.

Later that day, Patricia was excited (I mean VERY excited) because she could see in so much more detail with her new glasses than she could before.

"OMG! Why can I see everything in so much more detail than I could before this is so cool!" Patricia told her pet hamster (it was called Nala.

As she told Nala she saw her pull a confused face. Patricia mumbled something in amazement, "can you understand me or am I just going crazy?"

She noticed with her glasses that Nala nodded slowly. Patricia was ecstatic. She decided to keep it a secret and wanted to take Nala everywhere she went.

***

It was the next day and she had just arrived back from school. Patricia ran up to her room to see Nala(also to get changed into her Pjs). Patricia's Mam called her down to watch the news with her, so Patricia grabbed Nala carefully to watch TV with her Mam. As they were watching the news they heard that some people had stolen the Queen's priceless crown!

"Mam please let me go to London to try and find out who stole the crown I NEED to!" Patricia told her Mam and in that moment she told her Mam everything that had been going on.

"Fine you can go, but only if I can go with you," Patricia's Mam said with a sigh of defeat. So Patricia's Mam booked the train tickets to go to London.

***

It was the next day and Patricia was on the train with her mum and Nala. It took them a long time to get to London but in the end they arrived. Her Mam ran off into Primark or New Look or something like that. Then Patricia went off to find Buckingham Palace.

In a few minutes Patricia found it so she stepped inside.

"Ummm hi, I've come to try and find out who stole your crown Your Highness," Patricia said nervously.

As Patricia was studying the Palace, she found a pizza crumb and a strand of hair with her glasses. The Queen called the police to take the Queen, Patricia, Nala and her Mam to the pizza place to see who had stolen the crown.

A few exciting and worrying minutes later they had reached the pizza place. But there were two of them!

"Well, what are we going to do?" asked the Queen.

"I think we will have our chances with the one in front of us," said Patricia nervously. Patricia with her glasses (and her pet hamster Nala) tried to find the culprit of stealing the crown but there was no luck at that pizza place.

"It must be the one next door!" Patricia exclaimed. So they rushed next door with the clues in Patricia's hands. They burst through the door then Nala, who looked like a mini detective in Patricia's hand, sniffed out the culprit and then Patricia made sure that person was the culprit with her glasses. It was him because Patricia could see the pizza crumbs on his mouth. Then the police handcuffed the culprit and he got a death sentence.

So that is the end and that is how Patricia realized she had a superpower. Do you also want to know what happened to everyone else?

Ok then, I'm going to tell you, so Nala became Patricia's sidekick, the Queen got her crown back and Patricia became super popular(and I mean VERY popular).

Alien Opticians

By Martin at St Joseph's Primary School

Hi, this is Jake, an ordinary kid but with more liveliness. He had perfect vision and he thought that he would keep it, before it all went downhill. It all changed when he awoke to a crazy blur everywhere he went and because of that blur, at school he couldn't concentrate!

So his mum, as usual, got Jake in the glorious car, but instead of school they went to the opticians, because his mum was fed up of Jake not seeing well so she was going to get Jake's eyes tested. Hopefully he would get his glasses.

Time passed, as he waited for the journey to end. Jake moaned, "mum, where are we going?" but his mum, who was too concentrated on the road, didn't reply; she just wanted Jake to get his glasses. Then Jake turned to see, **"Charles' Optician"**? He thought he was going crazy and so he thought he needed to rest his head! (but little did he know it was just the blur of his eyes playing tricks on him!)

He slowly went inside... It just looked like a weirdly fashioned dentist's room. A strange, but boring room. But instead of teeth everywhere he looked, no no no... there were horrifying eyes basically everywhere! He was scared for his life! He then turned for his reassuring mum, but she was gone! ONLY EYES!

He fainted- then felt soft arms catching him in the act!

A voice gasped "Oh deary me, Jake! You have a dastardly fever!"

It was his mum... he had fainted.

All of a sudden, he awoke to see his room, which was strange, for he was at the opticians before. Then a voice spoke to him.

"Jake you're finally awake!"

"what happened?" he wondered, but his mum didn't care too much.

"That's for later, this is for now and now is the time for your glasses," his mum told him and so they travelled.

They arrived at the place where Jake was stopped by fainting. Then Jake again was stopped dead in his tracks, so his mum painfully dragged Jake until he could walk properly again.

Room A:
The main optician's room

"Ah Jake so glad to see you again!" an optimistic voice said... it was his DAD! "Now let me get your glasses, just wait here, it shouldn't take too long," he said.

Time passed, nothing.

Even later, still no sign of glasses. But then Jake heard something! But it gurgled horrifyingly "GLMFRAZ!"

Nervously Jake said "Hello? Is anyone there?"

Then... A giant glob of goop clashed straight at him! Jake struggled and wrestled, but the goop restricted him in a chair! He again struggled, but nothing happened!

Then the thing tried to put BRAINWASHING GOGGLES on him! He closed his eyes and waited for it to all be over...

Then as all hope seemed lost... nothing happened! He waited a bit more, but still nothing! He opened his eyes and everyone was back!

"Mum, what happened?" he pondered.

"That doesn't matter just go home with your glasses!" she leered.

"Then mum, what happened to the alien things, the eyes and the goo?" he was trying to ask, but was shut up by his mum saying "Just go home!"

Jake went home, put his glasses on his small drawer and he went to sleep.

He was changed and in his bed he slept like he had worked after a full time job.

When he slept he dreamt of the things that had happened that day. Maybe they were not real... UNTIL they snuck into his room. They shook him until he woke up and saw them. He tried to see if wearing his glasses would stop them from appearing, but nothing.

Ashley to the Rescue

By Evie at St Joseph's Primary School

Ashley was a normal girl who was just chilling on her bed, when suddenly, out of nowhere, she needed to get a drink. So she got up off her bed to see a large, black strip on her wall. But anywhere she looked, the black would go. She rubbed her eyes hard, wishing and hoping it was a dream, but the black strip didn't go away, it just got bigger. She went downstairs to tell her mam about it and her mam said to go to the opticians, looking scared, worried, sad.

They looked at it(her eye) and said that there was a black strip inside her eye!

Half an hour later, she went home to look at her eye again in the mirror and the strip had thankfully gone away but left her pupil to changed to a perfect heart. She acted like she was all ok, but, she knew she had a heart for a pupil. Which was weird but unique.

Early in the morning, she woke up and everything she looked at was zoomed in! She started to watch the news, minutes after she woke up, and found that there was a break-in!

"I wonder if they will be there again?" questioned Ashley to herself.

Ashley then rode rapidly on her bike down to the museum. She skidded at the museum (which was very big) and saw a person trying to steal an ornament from two miles away!

She sprang into action and caught the thief really quickly by leaping out from behind an exhibit and grabbing him by the leg. He crashed to the floor and Ashley dragged him up with his hands behind his back. She took him to the police station and explained what happened.

She was walking back to her house and met two girls who started beating her up. She was furious!

She went to school the next day and was perfectly fine. She didn't want to draw any attention to her eye. She walked into the classroom and nobody saw her eye, so, she did what she would normally do.

The bullies walked into Ashley's classroom and started to bully her again. They went to punch her but saw her eye. They thought it was cool and they wanted to be her friend, just because her eye was cool.

She knew what thy were doing so once they asked her, she said...

NO!

Ashley went outside to eat her lunch, and this girl came up to her. Ashley thought she was going to get bullied again but she didn't. The new girl wanted to be her friend and she didn't even know about her eye. They kept calling each other every night and then became best friends.

Gangster Granny and the Spy Glasses

By Divine at St Joseph's Primary School

Where am I? What am I doing next to a tree with a cat poster splattered onto it? I was in bed. Fast asleep. All I know is that I'm in a free world. No PARENTS. Well... I wouldn't say that free. Teachers. Old people. Not all of them were loving like Miss Dutchman. Not all of them were caring like Mrs Oldness.

Some old people admired the name Roxy. I don't know why they admired my name since it meant detective with bad eyesight. Really bad eyesight. Maybe they thought that because they were used to ancient names, according to teachers. Oh, I almost forgot; I haven't introduced myself. Now I have. Hahaha.

I caught something interesting just at that glimpse of the terrible eye of mine.

Cat missing
Super vision glasses for reward.

I had bad eyesight anyway. I still didn't understand how I had gotten here, you see. One minute later, just as I turned around, a granny who had grey hair stared at me. As she did that, she announced in a squeaky voice "those glasses are very special and have strong, microscopic ranges of colour as well as details to them.

"What, that can't be t..." before I could say 'true', she had gone. All I knew was that her first name was Cecilia.

Cecilia was old but smart. So I decided to search for the missing cat. After a few days of searching, I finally found it. After all my consideration, I finally decided to give the cat back to its rightful owner. It was one fluffy, white cat. It was heart-breaking to let it go. Just a few thoughts later, I decided to have a chat with Cecilia so she could team up with me. I knocked three times and Cecilia opened up.

"Hi," I said.

"Would you like to team up with me to catch the robber of the £500,000 mansion, jewellery and money?" I stammered.

"I've been waiting for you to say this, what are you waiting for? Let's get to it!" she exclaimed excitedly.

"I know you will love the name I am giving you.

GANGSTER GRANNY!"

Cecilia (Gangster Granny) loved the name. She was actually called Gangster Granny centuries ago because when she was young she did a lot of spying. A random question came into my mind, was she training or spying on me?

Since I had clothes for Halloween, and she had spy clothes from when she was young, finally we both decided to wear them. I wasn't sure if it would fit her, but surprisingly it did. Then we got the detective glasses. We hopped onto the motorbike and found our way to the police station.

We arrived at the police station and stood proudly in front of the policemen like we owned the place. We announced to them that we have come to track down the culprit of stolen money and jewellery.

They laughed. They burst. They roared until they couldn't stand. A few minutes later, they had calmed down and drove us to the mansion. We met a lovely lady called...

Read on to find out who this mystery lady is.

The mystery woman was Summer. She was a really nice lady. It took us thirty minutes to find the right room to look in since it was a mansion. We finally found it. There were auburn strands of hair all around Summer's bed. I finally got my super glasses on and found fingerprints of paint stains in the corner of Summer's room.

All in one blink, I called out to Granny, (who was drinking coffee) to get out my spy kit and the sellotape.

"Evidence 01!" I shouted with joy. I retrieved it in my bag.

"I'm very proud of you dearie," Granny replied. While she said she found the place where the treasure chest used to be.

There were strands of lavender curly hair around it. Not long after, I had the confidence to get out my spy glasses and scan it. You won't believe what I had just seen.

It was like a blossomy marshmallow colour and the spy glasses read that this person's hair was from the local supermarket. So I carefully placed the hair in the bag with tweezers and wrote "evidence 2".

"Woohoo!" I screamed. "I've done it again! With your help of course, Granny," I stated in my quietest voice.

"Obviously not."

I ran out with gangster granny and zoomed away to the supermarket.

We finally arrived and put on the super glasses and scanned and scanned. We finally found the culprit. I pounced out and shouted "got you now sucker!"

What an embarrassment. Now everyone was looking at me. Wow, so much for being a spy detective. After that embarrassment we hacked into the culprit's house to get the treasure chest. The thief was now in jail.

Summer appreciated it and gave us both a necklace. But there was something special about them, they were charms.

Without complaint we get a text. It was from the News around the world! We were in the newspaper! Everyone knew me and **GANGSTER GRANNY!**

All in five seconds flat my eyes started to flutter, they felt really, really sore. What was happening? Someone was shaking me?

...

Oh my goodness! you scared me mum. There were no adults when I was awake. Was all of this a dream, Granny?

Newspaper, police, necklace. 8:50.

It's time to go to school, I'm gonna be late!

"Calm down, I think you were in a fantasy dream world!" said mum worriedly.

"That means no granny, newspaper, police or necklace?" I questioned.

NO SUPER GLASSES FOR ME!

Detective Angela

By Laura at St Joseph's Primary School

One glamorous day, a little girl, who was called Angela, went into her garden to see if she could find some interesting and time taking mysteries to solve. She was ten years old and had long, blonde hair. Angela(who had sky blue eyes) wanted to become a detective when she grew up. BUT she would never solve any kind of mystery without her helpful dog Lucy. She was a golden retriever- which to me is the best kind of dog.

There was only one problem.

Quite a big problem actually.

Her vision was terrible. She saw every single thing with a blur. She refused to get her eyes tested because she was too scared. She didn't like going to the doctors either.

The next day, it got so terribly bad that she had to go. Her eyesight was way worse than before. She just had no choice.

So on the morning of the next day, her mam and dad drove her to the opticians. Angela, who didn't want to go at all, was miserable the whole ride there. When she arrived her mam booked her in and then they were sent to the waiting room. They waited for about ten minutes. But for some reason when she heard her name being called she put a smile on her face. She skipped cheerfully to the room she was supposed to. After she had her eyes checked the optician told her she had to wear glasses. She chose the pink, sparkly ones. When she got home it was late so she had to go to bed because it was school tomorrow.

When she woke up, which was at six in the morning, she had to get ready for school. She was a bit frightened because children might make fun of her. Her dad, who was called James, drove her to school before he went to work. When she cautiously walked into class the first thing she heard was kids laughing. Laughing. Kids called her mean names.

"Oh hi, stupid glasses girl!" said Grace in a loud voice so everyone could hear.

"Just leave me alone," whispered Angela. "those mean, naughty bullies."

At school they left her out of games and tried to hurt her. This carried on throughout the day. Luckily for her, it was the end of school. Her mam came for her. She jumped into the car and set off home.

While she was in the car, she realized she could see the smallest details. Later on in the day, her mam lost a sock while she was doing the washing. This was a perfect opportunity for Angela to try out her new vision. Suddenly, she saw the sock from A MILE AWAY! She ran over to it and shouted that she found it. Her mam was impressed that she found it effortlessly. Angela (who was even more impressed than her mam) was also really confused. But, she decided not to tell anyone. This was perfect because she loved being a detective. With her incredible glasses she could see fingerprints better than anyone. It was the end of the day, although it felt like an hour due to the joyfulness she felt. She went to bed quickly so that in the morning she could use her vision once again.

On Tuesday, in the morning, she randomly decided to walk to school. She was walking to school when she saw something strange on a lamppost. Each step she took she saw more and more clearly what it said. It was a poster which said:

Two thieves stole this 10,000 car.
If you see this car anywhere please contact 90145721
Any information will be helpful.
Thank you.

"Whoa, that IS a lot of money for a car!" said Angela, who sounded very shocked. She had to quickly put it in her bag because IT WAS SCHOOL IN 5 MINUTES!!! She ran like her life depended on it. When she arrived at school, she got bullied again but thankfully the school day passed by quickly. When it was over with she ran back home.

When Angela finally got home she was panting. She had run her fastest. Angela wanted to solve this mystery as fast as possible. It was time to call her trusty, detective dog Lucy.

"Lucy, come on! We have another mystery to solve!" shouted Angela. In a flash, she heard Lucy barking, which meant she was ready to solve mysteries. She told the dog everything about the thieves. She even showed her the poster! TO A DOG!! Lucy sat there. Maybe she understood. Maybe not. But she definitely listened.

She went outside with Lucy. Angela used her brilliant sight for hours but they had no luck. They found nothing. No clues. They gave up all hope. They started walking home but suddenly Angela stumbled. She looked what she fell over and it was A GLOVE! IT WAS a clue. She carefully picked it up and saw some fingerprints. Maybe they could finally figure it out. She gave it to Lucy and she sniffed it. Lucy started running. Angela ran after her. She could barely catch up with her. They ran, ran, ran.

When Lucy stopped running, Angela realized where she was. It was their old house! Angela was really confused. Why did she bring them here, she pondered. But when she turned around she couldn't believe her eyes. It was the stolen car!

"Well done Lucy. Good girl." she whispered. When she looked she saw the fingerprint. It looked like the exact same ones as on the glove. Maybe she had finally solved a real mystery!

She remembered that she had her phone in her pocket. She called the police immediately. They said they would come as fast as possible. The thieves ran so fast when they heard the police come that they were out of sight. Angela could see them perfectly. So she told them where they were. They got arrested and the car was given back to its owner.

Then they took Angela and Lucy to meet a real detective. They were really excited. The real detective gave Angela a special gold medal and he gave Lucy a bone which said thank you very much. She told them how much she wanted to become a detective and he told her that she would be accepted when she is older. She was the hero of the day. They said if not for her those thieves would have definitely got away. They were about to go off to France.

It was another day and once again it was school. Sadly, kids STILL bullied her. She knew it was because she was different. But she didn't care. She liked being herself. She didn't care what people thought about her anymore. She was herself.

That's all that mattered.

Hanna's glasses

By Eden at St Joseph's Primary School

Hello! My name is Hanna and I am 15 years old. My mam and dad are called Eve and Johnny, and I also have a dog called Lainey, who is a black Labrador. I go to St. Leonards' and I have 4 very trustworthy friends, Jack, Gabriella, Alexandra and Jane. Now I'm going to tell you about last summer when I got the shock of my life.

It was a normal day and I got ready to go to school and I got on the bus. When I arrived at school., I met up with Jack and Gabriella. My first class was art, which is the best class ever! After art it was break time, but I didn't do anything fun. Then it was topic. Very boring. Finally it was lunch. I sat next to Gabriella, who had pasta, and Jack, who had pizza. After lunch Jane invited me to Durham so I said "yes."

When I arrived at Durham, I saw Alexandra and Jane.

"Hi Hanna! How are you?"

"Hi Jane, hi Alexandra! I'm good thanks!" I replied.

Jane, Alexandra and I started shopping. After shopping, Jane and Alexandra were hungry so we went for dinner. I didn't have anything to eat because I was going out with my Mom and Dad. After we met a pretty, intelligent girl who showed us to the bus stop. She was very nice.

When I got home, I charged my phone and got ready to go out for dinner. When we arrived at the place we were going for dinner, I told them my order. It wasn't very complicated.

"Can I have a coke and a cheese burger?" I asked.

My Mom ordered a water and a pizza, and my Dad ordered a beer and a pasta. When we left, we saw a house on fire, so we went inside to save people. When I came out things started to go blurry. I felt someone grab my hand and they shoved me into a car. Everything went black.

When the car jerked to a stop, I came around with a jolt.

"Hey! Where am I?" I asked.

"Don't worry, it will be ok," said my Mom.

"That's not what I asked," I replied. But there was no reply. Right after my Mom took me into a shop. I knew it was a shop because I heard a bell ring.

After that I heard my Mom say "can I have an eye appointment please?"

That's all I heard. After that I felt something on my face, so I looked on my phone and saw that I had glasses!

The next morning, I was just sitting on my bed thinking if I should go to school. Then I thought people can say what they want to I don't care, so I went downstairs and asked my Mom if she could drive me to school and she said, "yes."

When I got to school, I kept getting complements, so I got more and more confident. I didn't mind glasses at all.

Well... I guess glasses are not as terrible as I thought.

Hero Glasses

By Kyle at St Joseph's Primary School

Since the day he was born being a Teenage Mutant Ninja Turtle, Raphael kept bumping into lamp posts and old shopping carts. He decided to visit the optician because he had been having so many accidents and he'd hurt himself so many times. The final straw came when he had a blow to his head after he struck it on a low sewer pipe as he walked along. He had been angry and frustrated, as well as having a huge bump on his head.

"Hello," he greeted the receptionist. "I need to have my eyes tested please," asked Raphael reluctantly as he did not want glasses.

Not long after, he chose the perfect pair, which were crimson red and jet black. Raphael put the glasses on. He didn't know what to think of them, but decided they were excellent. In a flash, the excellent glasses transported Raphael to a whole new world, and gave him super vision.

He was transported to an intergalactic space station, where there was lots of food (mostly pizza). Raphael discovered that he could see so many things: bedrooms, airlocks and a mining tunnel.

"Wow, this is a cool space station!" exclaimed Raphael.

He floated into the observation deck where he could see the stars also the planets that orbit the Sun and Earth facing the moon. From this perspective, the Earth looked so bright(the land appeared emerald green, whereas the oceans were cobalt blue.) He felt a little dazed due to the beauty of his home planet.

He suddenly found the space elevator and pressed the up button so the elevator could ascend. He stepped into the pod (grateful to not be having an accident). The door sealed and descended to the lower level of the station. As the pod door slid open, he found an alien containment facility with an alien inside. It was terrifying and bloodthirsty and it pressed its face against the glass. Raphael whipped off his glasses. He was back to super hero status.

Lewis and Luther

By Lewis at St Joseph's Primary School

World War III. 2088. Lewis was a sad and lonely boy - at only ten years old, he had spent half of his life (a whole five years) in an orphanage. It was a small leaning building which looked like it was about to collapse. His dad - a great soldier - died on the front line of the war, and his mam died from a great tragedy. She choked on a baked bean. (True story.) You see, he had no choice but to move into the ruined orphanage. He was made fun of, because he was legally blind, though he actually just had bad eye sight. Lewis could really use some luck.

One day when Lewis was meandering in the garden, he heard a voice. He thought it was Tiny Tom, who had a high-pitched voice, but then he realised the difference. Tom's never sounded angry(he was calm) and this one did!

"I said, do you mind? You nearly stepped on me!" shouted

Luther.

"HOW?!?" said Lewis.

"DUH. It's obvious. I'm just a snail," squeaked Luther.

"No, it's not obvious," raged Lewis.

"W-w-well give me one reason it's not obvious," said Luther.

"Mmm, let me think... maybe because I have bad eye-sight," sighed Lewis.

"Well, in that case, I can do you a favour," chuckled Luther.

***

The next morning, Lewis woke up. He thought all of what just happened was a dream. He felt a slight tingle in his eyes.

He. Could. Now. See.

"What the..... I can see!" screamed Lewis. He cried and cried with joy. He tried not to cry, so he could take a better look at the place. He stood still and studied the environment around him. He'd never seen the world with so much detail. He heard snores (loud ones) coming from his coat on his half-broken coat hanger, so he walked over. It was the same snail from before.

"What are you doing here?" whispered Lewis.

"Yaaaaaaaaaaaawwwwwwwwwwwwwwwwnnnnnnnnnn...
What???? I'm trying to get some sleep," whispered Luther, clearly half
asleep.

"How are you here?" shouted Lewis.

"Alright, alright. I get cold outside, so I snuck in your coat. And
anyway, I'm the one who made you see better. It was me, so you
should be thankful, not raging," squeaked Luther.

"Oh, no.... sorry, I didn't mean it that way, but did you really
make me see better?" said Lewis.

"Yes, I did. I said I'm magic, didn't I?" said Luther.

"Er, no you did not," back-answered Lewis.

"Ho," said Luther.

"Well, how rude of me. My name's Lewis," said Lewis.

"The name's Luther," said Luther, trying to act cool. "By the
way, I've started to realise people are always sad and crying," he
squeaked.

"It's World War Three. People are dying and we have no hope. I
mean - we're battling another planet!" explained Lewis softly.

"Ho, that makes sense. Well, who are we battling?" said Luther.

"Planet War," said Lewis.

"Well, at night, when every one's asleep, I'll show you something," said Luther.

***

At 11;05 that night, Luther and Lewis snuck out of the orphanage. When they got to the place, Luther made his way down the sewers, and Lewis followed on.

"L-L-Luther... I'm seeing perfectly clearly under a dark sewer," said Lewis.

"Did I mention you have night vision?" squeaked Luther.

"Thanks so much, but wow... this is amaz-- er, Luther? There is something over there," announced Lewis.

"It's what I came to show you!" said Luther.

When they arrived, Lewis pulled the towel off the object.

"It's a time machine! What do we do with it?" said Lewis.

"Obviously we're going to stop the war," replied Luther.

"Ok, but how?"

"Well, in space there's a man called Martin the Moon Walker, and he has a giant made from moons from all over the galaxy. It's called the Moon Boss. Martin the Moon Walker will get his giant to push Planet War away from Earth, but we'll have to go back ten days, because I heard that he destroyed the moon boss yesterday for no reason!" explained Luther.

"Yeah, but where is he?" said Lewis.

"Duh, on the moon... that's why he's called Martin the Moon walker."

"Might as well stop asking questions," said Lewis.

"Ok. Time machine, let's go to February 5th, 2088," said Luther.

When they were in the time machine, the noise was so loud Lewis's head felt like it was going to explode...

Lewis woke up in his bed. His eye-sight was blurry. But, when he looked on his window sill, he could see something special to him. His best friend, Luther, with more adventures to be found.

The Ultimate Glasses

By Cedric at Gilesgate Primary School

Part 1: A long walk in a broken picture frame

I don't know how I got here but it's creepy. I have spent the last few minutes walking through through an unstable picture frame and every minute I hear it creak. All I did was put on a pair of glasses and boom, everything I thought of came to life. Then I pictured a wormhole and I'm now in my fathers old picture frame bound to fall... So I guess I do know how I got here. HUH! All I wanted to do is see properly! I'll tell you how I got to this stale salvation of a desert.

Part 2: How it all started

I was riding my new dirt bike my Mama got me for my birthday. I went down the canals with Lola (my best friend) who was about to give me something special. She saved all her money - from chores and work- for them. A pair of glasses, she knew I needed them but didn't have enough to buy them.

When in class I started to dream... or not? I 'dreamed' that miss gave us a spelling test and every word I thought of she said. It got stranger until 'shfphhhh' a draft came from the window. It filled me with the memories of a man named Thauphet Haughton. He totally owned the universe. The glasses were the key, the glasses were stronger than the infinity gauntlet.

Later on that day my imaginary friends and I were having a meeting and everyone asked if I'd started a business. Then I realised I'd spawned them in. I was very happy about it at first but then I realised they could actually hurt me. This must be how Thauphet died, and now I'm trapped here, in this stupid old painting.

Part 3: The Power Development

Creak!

I knew I opened a wormhole here so I have to control my powers, but I have to be quick. I was getting a headache because of the thoughts all sinking into my brain. Then for once I looked at the stale environment. I felt the connection with my father and then he was transported into the painting with me.

"Well you've really done... wait you...you've got the Glasses Of Power. You did it Billy. You did it."

"did wha' Granda Jones."

"Ya found me brothers glasses holding the power of the gods."

I was so excited, I'd found the worlds biggest mystery of the infinite glasses of Thauphet who I've newly learned was a ruler who left the power for my herald. I didn't know what to say!

"He has created a magical bond with you son. You are God. Our leader. You are to be put upon the elites and rule them fourth to rule us. I'm proud of you son. Prouder than I'll ever be than anyone else in the world. You're my son!"

Part 4: When the Father Fades

Creak!

I was tearing up in pride.

When I went to wipe a tear the glasses slid off an inch and I returned back to my bedroom and my father at work. Just for that moment, my heart was filled with joy and my father had felt the same.

Meanwhile, in his fathers office.

"My son! My son got the glasses of power he was the herald!
My little Billy, he did it! My eyes were drowning in tears of pride.'

Jingle jangle!

"That was the bell everybody! That means you can leave
Percy's Purse until tomorrow, except for Jerome!" (Billy's dad).

"I'm having some worries about your son. If he has the glasses
he could be in mortal jeopardy. Remember how your brother Thauphet
died... he was killed by his own imagination. His own people banished
to the forest where he now rests. Do you want him to be the same?!"

"No sir, I didn't want him to be the herald!"

***

My dad's boss has worried me when he said how Thauphet
died, and again as I was thinking about his messages I was sucked into
the phone and it was like Metropolis. A great city was concealed with
inhabitants from the following: emoji, meme maker arcade games and
everything!

I went to the google station and asked what the glasses of power
were. It said that the gods had forged it with magic materials and half
of their powers to be passed through a certain blood line (the one that

Billy is unfortunately in)with one downside. All the people who take this emblem will meet a certain fate. This fate is that all their creations will turn against him or her.

He pointed to the owner of the google station the glasses and google shut itself down. Then he thought of his own world and realised what to do to harness his powers. He thought of a wormhole to go to a world of his own but he could breath in it.

Suddenly a wormhole appeared and he was in his own universe. Then he thought of himself as an immortal being and he imagined the earth built upon clouds with inhabitants to live on it, animals that did not need to waste. He named it Salvatiobilly a land of peace and immortality. His source of power, he summoned his family, friends and some holoschools (a school that is a virtual reality hologram).

I told them I was their king and they excepted that. They bowed down and worshipped me. Nothing bad could come out of a peaceful environment, could it? Well let's find out tomorrow.

***

I misjudged my statement, it's mayhem here. I knew I had to destroy the glasses before the whole world falls. I swiped the glasses off and tried burning them but it didn't work, then I realised I'd made everyone immortal in the land including ME.

I talked to them! gave them a lecture of peace then one said they were just putting on a play for 'his royal majesty' on the jester's order. I was in relief but also the deepest pain, I'd made a mockery of this land, I'd leave as tomorrow comes.

***

In the morning they begged me to stay, they needed a ruler to guide them so I said where'd you think I was going. They were in joy, "he was **staying!**" They were rejoicing and so they'd given me a blowing toy.

On my blow I'd turned myself into dust and instead of racing to the air I flew into their hearts and they themselves became the people yielding the gods power and reducing it into good. They memorialised me and became their own leaders but still a pack of friends.

The new adventures to be held for the glasses will be better than mine hopefully and they wouldn't die out as soon as mine did.

To Be Continued...

The Ultimate Glasses Part 2

By Cedric at Gilesgate Primary School

When my son died we were all sad. Even happy emoji was crying. Me and my new mate buried him under the throne and covered his grave with fresh soil wet from tears. Silently, we tiptoed away with our heads buried in our hands.

Every time we had felt ourselves of no importance he was there to comfort us. My mate (his da') and I don't know what to do. We thought we could go to his old picture frame and forget about it. The phrase 'with age comes wisdom' was in fact true and since they had wisdom they learned a lot quicker on how to harness their powers.

After transporting to it, they realised they had never been in such a quiet environment. It was a dull yet peaceful surrounding and one of the best p/aces to clear your head. The only down side was that it barely had light so he created a wormhole to just a living room in the middle of a void.

Every time he went through the portal he got weaker. Because of this, he could barely walk. He decided to sit on the sofa and regain strength for eternity.

Meanwhile, I was crying which is very unusual as I'm a happy emoji from his fathers phone. Its frustrating how he just vanished and didn't give me any of his dust. I'm possibly the only one who didn't get it. Now I'm out-raged.

I need to get home. Back to the phone I lived in... Huh.

I'm probably never going to though. My wife and my wife's children depend upon it. I wish for just one day I'd be at peace with my family and new/old friends.

***

I miss Billy already. He was my brother in combat. A best friend and without him around to tell us what to do I'm lost. He was an eye opener that would speak for the speechless. He'd try to do the right thing and for that I am forever in his debt.

Billy created me and raised me from an egg. A dragon egg he'd pictured in his mind and gave the inner dragon, me, the ability of speech. He loved me and cared for me. My father never did anything bad. He was my hero and adding to that, a loving father.

He would cry at death and rejoice at birth. He was everybody's hero. Especially mine –Karlasta– a great warrior but also a great friend. And he again created me, raising me –like all of them-- from a baby.

Billy was my staggering enemy but I saw a light shine in him before he died and that light changed my heart. We had many different battles in different locations but that was all in the past. I'd made it history. I'm gonna miss him as he was a good sport.

He'd changed us all!

But wait... there's still one more twist to this story. The dust started to leave people's bodies. It joined at his grave and just like that emerged for the last time, **Billy***! He had said in very leader worthy words, "looks like you needed me after all, huh!"*

Everybody's glasses snapped off but they didn't care. Their leader was back. Everybody was back in Salvatiobilly (a land of his work) to witness it! A land of his creativity. A land of excitement that everybody wished for but most of all home.

The people of Salvatiobilly once more had a reason to rejoice. They celebrated by building many holostructures for him including a celebratory bar for him to drink the lights out of himself. He was pleased with the environment he had created.

***

"Dad, do you remember how mom died!" Billy asked.

And dads responding was quite severe. "A man Davison Andrews assassinated h er thinking she was Dailer Sheirar a traitorous monster!"

"So that's show she died?"

"No she saw him coming, after that she walked into the road with a bus following!"

" Well I can bring her back. So you should stand back!"

***

I was in complete shock laying eyes on her! She gained eye contact and that's all I can re... remember. Now I'm lying in a hospital bed looking my son in the eye. Where was my wife? I thought with the crows cawing.

I know I'd been dead but I could still control my power. I read his mind and told him she went home. He cried out large tears until waterfalls emerged into his eyes. They fell to the floor.

Then when they stopped he began. He plunged to his death. Unfortunately, I could not prevent this. I used all my power but it wasn't good enough. His face had hit the floor. He was dead. I couldn't even bring him back from his newly crowned grave.

I cried remorselessly until the kingdom came to comfort me in my darkest hour. They Told me some things and then the darkness transformed to light. The darkest hour possibly became the lightest.

The kingdom had proven they were trust worthy. They told me the the things they said about me. And they said it from the heart. Even my worst enemy was nice. It's sweet what they had said and I would treasure those moments.

I returned to my throne. The first thing I created but wished for somebody else to sit upon it. I guess they did need me as a leader though for when I died madness stole into their heads. They loved me!

The End

The Girl with Glasses

By Mildred at St Joseph's Primary School

In the south of England –in London– in a nearby university called Saint Mary University, there was a young woman (a student to be precise) named Luna and she had a pretty bunch of friends. Their names were Sophie (her best friend), Kai (also her best friend), Jessica (a good friend but dislikes Luna a lot) and lastly Alex (another good friend and he also dislikes Luna but is ok with the idea of being her friend). Ok now that I have talked to you about the introduction to my story, let us get right into the story shall we?

In the morning –at 6:45– Luna got ready for school and as she was getting ready, she could not see very well but she didn't care. Then she had some breakfast, she got in her car and drove to her school/the University (which was 15 minutes away).

Now, we shall see what will happen to Luna. Will she still not care about how she could not see very well? Or will something happen?

Let us find out. After 15 minutes of driving, Luna arrived at the University, the time was 7:05am when she got there and it was a good thing she arrived at this time because school/lessons began at 7:15am. So she had time to talk to her friends. When she saw her friends she was really happy. After talking for 15 minutes straight, the bell rang and classes started. In class the teacher (Mr William) saw that Luna was finding it hard to see the board.

After school, Luna said good-bye to her friends and as she was about to go home, she was confronted by Mr William and he said "Young mistress I think you might need glasses because you seem to be struggling to see the board."

Luna replied, "I see, ok Mr William."

"Brilliant! Now if you excuse me I will be off to work," exclaimed Mr William

Luna said, "Bye see you tomorrow."

When Luna got out of the University, she went to the opticians and when she finished getting her glasses, she hated them or that is what she thought. When she got to school the next day, she forgot to take off her glasses so one person saw her but did nothing just took a lot of pictures and spread fake rumours (did you find out who it was?

It was Jessica). When Luna went to her friends, Jessica left and Alex followed her and Luna shouted "Hey guys why did you leave?"

Alex replied shouting, "Because you made fun of us!"

Luna was confused, she wondered who or even what made them this way and how can she change them back. She looked at her two best friends and asked, "what happened to them they were never like this before?"

Kai and Sophie asked, "Is it true?"

Luna replied, "Is what true?" now Luna was as confused as a newborn.

"That you called us and our families aliens?!" shouted both Kai and Sophie.

"NO! Why would I? you guys are my best friends I would never!"

"Oh ok that makes me so happy," exclaimed Kai and Sophie.

"Don't worry guys I would never be that rude," said Luna.

"We are all best friends!" yelled Sophie

"And we will always be!" replied Luna

"Yes we will, oh I wanted to ask why do you have glasses Luna?" said Kai.

"Because I need them and I actually like them I guess," exclaimed Luna.

"Oh ok then," replied Kai and Sophie.

As the day went on, Luna wanted to know what made Jessica and Alex like this. Before they were like children always looking up to Luna, but now they just left and walked off like they saw a spider, in her mind all she could think about was "what did I do wrong? Either way they are gone now so let me not get so down now but the main thing is my new glasses are so useful I can see so well now!"

As the lesson went on, Luna could see everything so clearly -1 mean she could see fine before but now she could see as if she had binoculars on and she was doing so much better now.

When school had ended, Kai and Sophie told Luna about a 1 million pound Lottery and she shouted "we should enter it we might have a chance win!"

"Ok," exclaimed Sophie and Kai.

At the Lottery place, Luna, Sophie and Kai entered the lottery and happily Luna could clearly the numbers on her Lottery ticket, as they were about to go out of the ha ll were the Lottery was held they saw Alex and Jessica.

Alex shouted, "What are you doing here with her!"

"We came to enter the Lottery and-," said Sophie but was soon interrupted by Kai.

He exclaimed "–And she is our best friend unlike you so now answer this, why are you here, are you here for the Lottery or are you following us like a book follows its owner?"

Jessica replied "we are hare for the Lottery, not for you or your 'friends'." Somehow right after Jessica said that Luna immediately knew that she was following them. She thought that it might have been her glasses that warned her of Jessica and Alex's plans.

The next day –it was a Saturday luckily– Luna woke up because her phone rang.

Sophie facetimed her and exclaimed, "Hey bestie!"

Luna put on her glasses and said "Hey, what's up?"

"Can I come round so we can do our homework together?" asked Sophie.

"Sure, come in 20 minutes," replied Luna.

"Why 20 minutes I can just drive the- wait have you just woken up?" asked Sophie.

"Yes," said Luna.

"Oh, ok then! I will see you in 20 minutes!" exclaimed Sophie.

"Ok, see you then."

After the call/face time, Luna got out of bead and when she had finished getting ready she called Sophie and asked "Hey! Where are you?"

Sophie replied, "I'm in front of your house silly!"

"Oh ok I'm coming," exclaimed Luna with her glasses on. When Luna opened the door for Sophie she came in and they talked for 50 minutes straight and Luna told her how well she could now see because of her glasses and that how she hopes that one of her friends win the lottery or maybe even her.

After talking for so long, Sophie and Luna remember about the Lottery and ran to Luna's car and drove to the Lottery place and Luna forgot her glasses but luckily, Sophie got them so she was able to drive and she could see her ticket.

When they arrived they saw Kai, Alex, Jessica and a lot of other people with tickets in their hands. Luna and Sophie walked and met up with Kai and when the lottery started, the person who was in charge of the Lottery came. "Alright the number that wins is 48967!"

No one shouted "I GOT IT!" until...

"I'VE GOT IT I'VE GOT IT!" shouted Luna! She was so happy that she could see the numbers because of her glasses and that she won.

"Come and get your prize young lady!"

"Ok!" She replied happily and when she got on the stage she was given her prize money. Although everyone was sad that they didn't win but they were happy for Luna and clapped for her but on the other hand, Jessica and Alex were so angry and they stomped out of the Lottery place/Hall, as they were exiting Luna with her glasses could see that Alex was sad but he was too shy to say it, so he stomped out of the Lottery Place with Jessica pretending to be angry. When Luna got down she was holding a suitcase (which was filled with money, her money) and she was happy not just because she won, because she could see what was happening and everyone's nice smiles and how she could see how cool glasses are.

As the people in the Lottery place started to leave, Luna, Sophie and Kai were starting to finish their chatter and said good-bye to each other. They all went home. Sophie went with Luna because her car was at her house and because she lived really close to her.

I guess that wraps up that, let us continue from where we left off shall we?

The next day at the university everyone was hugging Luna because she had won the Lottery and a part of those who were in the crowd. Alex and Jessica were also in the crowd and they thought that Luna would forgive them this is how it went out:

"Hi Luna," said Alex. "want to be our friend again?" asked Alex.

"Let's see, ok," joked Luna.

"Really?" exclaimed Jessica.

"Of course," said Luna "...Not!" she exclaimed.

"W-what!? Why?" asked Alex and Jessica.

"Well let's see... you said a lie to Kai and Sophie saying I called them and their families aliens," exclaimed Luna.

"Wait you didn't call their families' aliens and you didn't call me and my family a slug?"Asked Alex, at this time Jessica was slowly creeping away but Alex grabbed her hand.

Luna could see how scared Jessica was and how angry Alex looked thanks to her glasses, which at this point she thinks they gave her like super vision so she could see the tiniest of things.

Luna said, "of course not! I would never call my friends or their families aliens or slugs! I love you guys you're like a family to me and I like that none of you laughed at my glasses, I for sure thought that you would laugh at me but you didn't so that is why you guys are so dear to me!"

"So you lied to me," Said Alex looking at Jessica and little did anyone but Luna know because of her glasses, that Jessica was sweating like mad. Luna could see the little particles of salt in her sweat.

After being yelled at by Alex, Jessica said in a very soft voice "I-I'm sorry!" it was hard to forgive her but Luna, Kai, Sophie and Alex found it in their hearts to forgive her.

So they all became friends again and Luna told them about her super vision that her glasses gave her. They were all surprised of what she said and that was "With these glasses I can see everything that normal eyes can't see!"

They were all confused but they still stayed her friend. So this is the end and what happened Luna was rich and she always gave some money to the poor. Well that is what happened and the moral of the story is don't spread rumours, True or Fake, and always be a good person of the society and others. If you need glasses don't be scared to get them because even if you get bullied tell an adult or just ignore them, then tell an adult. Always tell an adult, never fight back and who knows, maybe you can get super vision like Luna!

So what I am trying to say is that always be kind to others.

The Green Eyed Monster

By Charlotte at Belmont Community School

Today, was my second ever eye test. I wasn't nervous. The first time, I actually quite enjoyed the opticians. Until the very end that was, it was explained to me that I had 20/20 vision (completely perfect eyesight). I hysterically sobbed that day, my dream has always been to wear glasses (and now my dream had been crushed).

However, recently I've had some difficulty reading. Hopefully, today is my lucky day - the day my biggest dream will come true.

I sat in the cold chair and braced myself for the absolute worst result. I was told to attempt to read the eye chart. However, I couldn't. All the letters were moving : or upside down. The optician soon after diagnosed me with dyslexia. However, I didn't mind, in fact I was overjoyed, because it meant I needed glasses!

I woke up the next day - a giant smile on my face. The first thing I did was race to put on my new glasses. After quickly getting dressed into my school uniform, I sprinted to school - eager to show off my new accessory.

Except, I didn't receive the love I expected. Instead I was bullied and harassed by the other students. They were vicious and called me disgraceful names; names like four eyes or swat. I went home crying that day. After explaining why I was crying to my mother, she sat me down and told me something. She told me that others were just jealous.

The green eyed monster had officially arrived...

Cosmic Glasses

By Casey at Belmont Community School

I was dreading getting my glasses today. Mikey had gotten some glasses yesterday and she was getting the absolute mick taken out of her. Jam Jars was her nickname now; I didn't want to be that person.

A frown on my face, I walk into the opticians and pull my messy auburn hair into a jumbled bun. My name was called in to get my accessory so I trudged into his office, clearly in distress. The pair my mother had picked out for me were quite nice however, I still didn't want to risk being the victim in hell, or school as normal people called it. The cosmic circular frame and glass lens shone in the golden sunlight. Particles floated about the room only visible when the star provided the room with light. It made them seem majestic.

I was suddenly hit with excitement! Who cares what other people think about me? As long as I'm happy. I place the gadget on my face, fitting them perfectly on my ears. Looking into the mirror, I admire how the shape goes well with my facial structure. I loved them, they made me feel enlightened, happy almost.

My mother and I leave the building and hop into the car, me wriggling with excitement to show my dad my new glasses. We arrive at home and I speed into the living room, where my dad was asleep in a chair, newspaper on his lap.

"Dad.. Dad!". He jumps a little and adjusts his trim. I stand proudly presenting my new glasses.

He smiles at me, "They're lovely pet....."

His eyes slowly close again, and snoring is heard within the next 30 seconds.

I giggle at him and go upstairs to send a picture of my new accessory to my friends.

Trepidation

By Eve at Belmont Community School

It was the day, the day I got my new glasses; they are going to be the only things that will change my whole entire life forever. Wearing glasses is actually horrendous, they basically take over your life, people say "Oh you're a swot, nerd, geek or a try hard!" and those are really not the the names you want to be called in Year 8.

Reputation is key while being a 13 year old - reputation is EVERYTHING!

I was sat in silence in the car with my Mam in a right huff with myself and she said, "You'll love them Eve honestly trust me," and my response was silence, absolute silence.

The optician was around the corner and my only thought was, "What if I see the boy I like from school is in Durham right now?!" My heart was literally was pounding in my throat.

Thank god I didn't see him - my life would've been over. My Mam opened the door and reality all of a sudden hit my like a massive wave while been in the sea at the beach, what if I actually look sort of alright in glasses?

What if the boy I like actually thinks I look quite cute with glasses on...

Goggle

By Kayla at Belmont Community School

It was Angus' first day of primary school with his new glasses (Goggle). Angus loved talking to Goggle as he always understood how Angus was feeling.

"Have a good day Angus! Make sure you don't lose little Goggle!" whispered Angus' mum as she kissed him goodbye.

"I know mummy, I'll be careful!" said Angus as he began to walk into his brand new school.

When Angus went into his classroom he was met with a bright range of blurry colours that he could not really see so he put his glasses on. Goggle blinked as he cleared Angus' vision so he could admire his beautiful new classroom!

Suddenly, Goggle sneezed and jumped abruptly away from

Angus and towards the nearest fluffy bear toy.

"Angus! Don't throw your glasses, you could break them!" shouted the teacher.

"Miss I didn't! Goggle just sneezed!" exclaimed Angus.

All the children around him laughed and joked while Angus sat in the corner extremely upset. The teacher called Angus' mum who soon arrived and hugged Angus lovingly until he stopped crying.

"Angus," she said "I know you are upset but it really doesn't matter about what the other kids think of you because you're always perfect to someone!" she whispered as she held him close.

After Angus' mum left, Goggle came up to Angus and snuggled into his shoulder. Friends like Goggle come and go but your family is forever.

Gaming Glasses

By Jared at Belmont Community School

"You need to stop sitting so close to the TV, Jack!" said Emma. He refused to move, almost at the end of a game of FUT Champions on FIFA. He really was sitting a little too close, but he always made the excuse that he couldn't concentrate unless he was close.

Later on that day, his hands trembled with fear as he brushed his teeth. He acted like he didn't care about his eyes but, inside, he did care. Barely being able to see 5+ metres away, he was afraid he did have a real problem with his eyes. He didn't want to tell Emma, his mother, in fear that she would get mad at him for all the combined hours spent on his PS4 20cm away from the screen. But in reality, she did have a suspicion of a problem with his eyes, and she wasn't mad at him.

After 5 hours of sleep of the endless thought of the opticians, it was the big day. His hands shook as his mam parked outside the Simon Berry Optometrist. All fear was lost as he noticed how calming the shop was. It gave him a warm feeling, and he was no longer scared.

He needed glasses.

Emotions built up as he heard those words but he noticed that it is better for him. He could finally see well without problem. School the next day was a scary prospect, but he got through it with many compliments and nobody being mean towards him. Glasses were the right option.

Laser surgery

By Hayden at Belmont Community School

It was the day of my first laser test. I'm shaking in fear of the lasers near my eyes. If only I wore my glasses once I was told to. Anyway, it's only 30 minutes until my operation. I'm dreading this as I don't want to get a laser op. The terrifying, tiny laser will leave me scared of them for a while. I hope that I don't get poked in the eye when I'm playing football on Saturday. Especially as it's against our rivals, so I better be okay.

Now it's time for me to go in for op, I hope it goes well...

***

I've just woke up from the op, my eye stinging and burning. I've never felt pain like it! At least I was asleep so it wasn't too bad... only joking, it was absolutely killing me! My mum asked me "you going to play tomorrow?"

I simply shrugged my shoulders, but inside I knew that I would be able to play tomorrow. I had a problem with my eyes because I used to stand too close to my TV when playing a game on my Xbox(mainly FIFA). If I didn't get my operation, I would have gone permanently blind(which I obviously didn't want).

Now, all I want to do is go home. I'm in too much pain to be awake, I need to go to sleep. I really don't want to keep writing this down, so I'm going to stop and get some much needed sleep...

Jack's Glasses

By Ben at Belmont Community School

It was the day before Jack was getting his glasses. He was really nervous and excited; he would be able to see properly for the first time.

Jack was a normal 7 year old boy, but with a difference- he couldn't see properly because of a sight problem which he got when he was only two. After 5 years of struggle, he now wanted to try to wear glasses to help him.

After a sleepless night it was time; Jack was going to get his glasses and maybe see properly for once. He was really nervous because he didn't know what was going to happen and if it would even help him. Shaking with nerves, he entered the opticians and was greeted by Simon Berry (the optometrist). With thoughts filling his head, Jack was calmed by pictures on the walls.

Jack was now relaxed and ready to complete his eye test to see what glasses he would need to wear. However, he struggled with the eye test.

After the eye test he was filled with a warm feeling that he would be able to finally see like a normal person. This meant that he would now see the world in a whole different way.

The new glasses made Jack view the world in a whole new way and could now do everything his friends were doing. However he didn't like wearing his glasses because he thought they didn't look good on him. But he knew he had to wear them to be able to see properly.

After many years Jack didn't mind wearing his glasses. He was very thankful for his glasses and for Simon Berry making possible for him to see properly.

Jared's Test

By Jack at Belmont Community School

It was the night before Jared's very first eye test, his hands trembled in nerve. He shut his eyes in hope to get to sleep however sleep wouldn't come to him. It was the school holidays and Jared was worried about getting glasses for the six weeks off - he was worried about people making fun of him.

It was Monday morning and the first day of the summer holiday but Jared had to go for his very first eye test. His mam woke him up ready for a big day in his so far small and young life. It was 10 o'clock in the morning and Jared was on his way to the opticians.

His mam took him to the waiting room; he took his seat there. His appointment was due any minute now. "Can we have Jared Readman in room 1 please," called out the optician in a warm and welcoming voice. Jared stepped through the doors of the room cautiously, however the optician reassured him that everything would be alright had that there was nothing to worry about. Pictures hung on every wall which calmed Jared's nerves immediately.

Jared was now relaxed and ready for his eye test, it was time to see if he needed glasses. However he struggled with the test and the optician announced the words that he needed glasses. He tried on different glasses to see what fit he would need, he tried on one pair of glasses and knew straight away that these were the glasses he wanted. He now forgot all about what his friends thought and decided that wearing glasses is what's best for him.

A girl called Jasmine

By Josane at St Joseph's primary school

There's a girl called Jasmine who lives with her mum Sarah. Her dad, Jonathan, went to go and serve in the army. He visited her when she was 6. She had only seen him once when he came home from the army and Jasmine hadn't seen her dad for three years. Now she is 9 but still feels sad. She feels even more upset when she goes to school because she has no friends and always gets bullied.

One day at school she sat at the back of the classroom and she found it hard to see. Jasmine asked the teacher if she could move but when she did it didn't get any better. All she could see is blurry numbers. At the end of the day the teacher gave them homework about what they want to be when they are older.

Jasmine's mum took her to the opticians because she could only see things blurry no matter how many times she had to rub her eyes it was still no good. Jasmine got her eyes checked and the opticians said that she needs some glasses. They were the side effects what happen when you don't wear them so it wasn't really a big deal.

The next morning Jasmine had a P.E. lesson and they had to practice cross country. After running for half an hour they got a five minute break. Aimee and Alana (the two bullies) came up to her and said "you're looking thirsty, here have some water!"

She opened the water bottle up and threw all the water on Jasmine. She was wet from head to toe.

Jasmine fell to the ground and her glasses slid off her head onto the floor, and Alana ran and crushed them to pieces.

A boy called Stuart felt really bad for Jasmine and decided to help her up and gave her a tissue to dry her face. Soon after they became friends and jogged along with her during cross country practice. When Jasmine got home from school she was furious with Aimee and Alana so she got the phone and rang the school!

Sarah (Jasmine's mum) told Jasmine to get her coat because they needed to get two new pairs of glasses from the opticians in case one of them broke – again. Once they had bought the glasses by the time they got home it was dark.

When they got into the house they could hear barking and saw someone sitting on the sofa – It was her dad. He was holding a

Dalmatian puppy which was for Jasmine to make up for all the birthdays he had missed of her! She named the dog spotty and gave her dad a big hug.

Today was Jasmine's birthday. It was on a Sunday. She had a house party and her gran, grandad, Stuart, her mam and dad all came. Stuart gave her a new and customised glasses case and sides of glasses. Her parents got her a phone and a bike. Her gran and grandad got her some money and an iPad.

It was the next day and all of a sudden people started being nice and friendly to her and she gained a few more friends but Stuart was still her very best friend. Once she saw Alana and Aimee she immediately walked the opposite way to them. They went after her and she eventually stopped running. They apologized to her and then they didn't become friends but they didn't become enemies.

Searching the Ashes

By Isaac at St Joseph's primary school

Harry one morning gets up on a cold winter's morning, ready to go to his factory to work. So he said goodbye to his family and opened his blackout curtains only to find half of London had been disintegrated by rushing explosions of gunpowder all over the helpless city.

He was bewildered with what was going on, then as quick as a flash, Harry sprinted upstairs to share this horrible sight he saw.

But as soon as he got into the mediocre room, no-one was there... he searched and searched and searched but there was no sign of anyone being found. He had one last resort, and that was to set out, to find his mum and find somewhere safe and secure. Firstly, he had to pack everything up, secondly he had to make sure everything was okay outside and finally he set off.

Stupidly, Harry went through all the crashes and flash bangs to find his mum, then half disoriented Harry stumbled on a non-lethal grenade and before he had time to react...

BANG!!

it sent Harry and his glasses flying off into the cold, deserted terrain. Dark thoughts crept into his mind and he had finally lost hope, he was dead for sure now.

But Harry took all he could gather to stand up and started searching for help. Then when everything was blurry Harry could faintly see an outline of his glasses. Gasping with joy he reached for them and was pulled back by an anxious shaky hand.

It was unknown who it was, until he heard his mum's voice saying "Harry, it's me!"

Harry was crying tears of joy but he couldn't see at all.

A few months later Harry's mum took him to Simon Berry's and gave him a perfect pair of glasses which were 10 times better than his normal pair. Then they started their lives again, moving to a new country.

Australian Glasses

By Vanessa at St Joseph's primary school

One sunny morning, a lady, not very young; was called Anne. Anne was 38. She loved to work. Her husband (Thomas) was age 36. He had to go to wok every day. Their son was 2 and his name was Harrison. Also, they had a daughter named Amy. She was 16. All of them were packing because that afternoon, they were going to go on a plane; for the first time. To leave their country and go to Australia for the Easter holidays.

There was one problem for the 16-year-old (Amy)...

Of course, it was because she didn't have enough room in her suitcase to fit more of her beautiful clothes and makeup. Also, she remembered that today they had to go for the last day of school before the Easter holidays. Unfortunately, they were going to have tests all day long.

On the other hand, Harrison was really excited because they were going to have an Easter party! Every year, the Easter Bunny would come and hide chocolate eggs all around the classroom and they would have to find their name. If they found one that wasn't with your name but someone else's, you would have to give it to the person that it actually says. Harrison had been the first one in class. Everyone had finally come into class.

The teacher called out "let the Scavenger Hunt begin!"

Everyone started looking for a present or an Easter egg with their name on. Finally, Harrison found one. He couldn't read the name, though. That ruined his day, a lot.

Finally, the teacher realised, and took him to the nursery's opticians. His mum and dad rushed up the stairs to find Harrison. When they found him, they grabbed him without realizing he needed glasses, eve though they knew they were in the opticians. The baby was trying to get his parents attention, but they didn't care and they just carried on walking back home. They were too concentrated on going on holiday. They did not want to be late. As they were flying in the plane the baby was trying to get his parents attention again, but again they ignored him.

At last, they got to Australia. In the car the mum was playing games with the baby and when they got to the game, 'Number Cards', he couldn't read the numbers and the mum finally realized that he had bad eyes. They took him to the opticians in Australia. When they got there it looked kind of strange to them. They didn't care, and went inside.

The lady had realized that he had really bad eyes when they gave him super glasses ones that no-one has had before...

In a split second, he started floating. He went up in the sky. The baby loved it. He landed back down. He could see everything much better. He also had a superpower which was night vision.

Dave the Blind

By Ryan at Trinity School

*This story is dedicated to the author's grandmother,
Joyce, for keeping him supplied with pens and paper so
he could practice the art of storytelling.*

Part 1: Once upon a time...

Once upon a time, there was a 13 year-old boy named Dave and he is so blind that the only colour he sees is black and white. He had a family so his parents did not ask for help so they told him his turtle, Rudolph, wants some food, so he gets some food.

But he forgot that he's still blind, so Dave gave Rudolph the wrong food. His Mam, Susan and Aidan laughed. Meanwhile, Dave wants to have a date with Rosie so Dave asked his parents and his parents said yes, so Susan called Rosie and asked Rosie and Rosie said yes. So Dave and Rosie went to a burger bar.

Dave wants salad and Rosie wants some chicken nuggets.

So Dave eats the chicken nugget and...

….....

He was barfing.

So Rosie said "HAAAAHAHAHAHAHAHAHAHAAHAHA!"

Rosie laughed.

So Dave and Rosie got home.

It all started 2 years and 11 days ago.

Part 2: 2 years and 11 days ago

The solar eclipse came on. Everyone came and celebrate but Dave forgot to wear specular glasses so Dave got blind. So back to the prrreesssent Dave told his parrrrrreeennntsss he had enough and wants to buy some glasses but Aiden asked if he wants some contact lenses and Dave said yes so Aiden drives Dave to the opticians. So Josh Wells gave Dave some contact lenses but they melteddddd so Dave tried some glassesssssssss and they worked.

Davvvveeee coulddddd seeeee evverrrrything the nexxt dayyy the mathss teacherrr asked Dave what 222+11x9999 is.

Dave said 1,100,211.

Ryan Jackson tells Dave to come up to the board.

Dave goes to the board.

Board says 111198x999923=

Dave said 111,189,437,754.

Dave got an S+++ +++

Part 3: Four Eyes

So they called him four-eyes, beer, brady, snitter, balloon, rock, cocktail, highballlllllll lllliqueur, lowball, and haarrrrrry potttter.

Day after day they are stilllllll making fun of him.

So dave had enough and telllllllllllllll themmmmmmm whyyyyyyy he wears glassesssss. So he said ouurrrrrrrr eyes have eeeeeeeyyyyyeeballs. To understandddd whyyyyyy a few people wear glassesss we firrrrst need to know more about the eyes. On the eye we have two major parts the cornea and the lens or the baccccccccckkkk ttthhherrrreeeeeees another part that is called the retinaaaaa. The lens and the corneaaa woooork togetherrrrrrrrrrrrrrrrrrrrrrrrrrrrrrrrrrrrrrrrrrrr soooooooooooooooo that lighhhhht raysssss frommmmm outside ooooobjectsss can come insidee thhhhe retinaaaaa.

Theeeeeeee retina is the place where we have cells that can detect light. Let's see, when light rays get focused in front of the retina these people are called myopic. They can see nearby objects clearly but are not able to see distant objects. They are also called short-sighted. Now let's see what happens when outside light is focused behind ttthhheee retina these people are called hyper optic.

Rosie said "hyper optic means longsighted," and Dave said yes.

These people are able to see things far away very well, but they can't see nearby things.

The other students said "you also wear glasses... are you short-sighted or long-sighted?"

Dave said "I am long sighted, I can see the sky very clearly, but I can't rrread a book without my glasses. Few have the shortest eyeballs and few have longer eyeballs.

Light rays get focused in front of your rrrrrrrrrretina... you can see these up close, and struggle with things in the distance.

The students understand and........

Said "soorrrrrrrry."

Becky: my sister in law with glasses

By James at Trinity School

My sister in law went to the optician for her eye test. She said that it went really well. When she finished her eye test she got her result – if she needed glasses or not. Becky has to wear glasses because her eyes were not that strong.

Becky felt really excited at first but then she felt embarrassed that she had to wear glasses. She picked out some really good glasses. They were pink and blue ones.

The next day my sister in law went to school with her new glasses but she didn't want to wear them for school. She didn't want to wear them because she thought her friends would make fun of her and she would feel upset. When she got to school she had taken them off so nobody could make fun of her.

Before Becky got home she put them back on so that her mam would think that she had had them on.

About a year later Becky has decided to wear her glasses from now on because her sister said that she looks older in them. No one ever made fun of Becky or made her feel upset.

The New Boy

By Sophie at Trinity School

One day this girl didn't want to have glasses because "my friends might laugh at me."

The next day a new boy came in. Then the boy was getting bullied and the girl came over and said "I got bullied too... and it doesn't matter if you have glasses or not you shouldn't get judged."

She bumped into the lamppost and fell on her knees and she was crying and begging.

And she said, "it is ok for people to have glasses. People shouldn't judge others on whether they have glasses or not. Everyone has their personality and their opinion. But don't get upset about it."

Afterword

By Simon Berry

I hope you have enjoyed these stories.

This may be the first Gilesgate Story Challenge but it is only the beginning. Our hope is that this competition will run every year and grow from strength to strength.

This first competition was about eyes because I am an Optometrist.

Next year we are looking for businesses or organisations to take on the challenge and create their own competition and subject.

So if you have a local business and would like to be involved, let me know.

I hope the Gilesgate Story Challenge will grow from strength to strength and inspire more and more children each year.

About Simon Berry

Simon has been an Optometrist for over 20 years. He opened his own community Practice in Gilesgate in 2002.

This year he has launched a device to help Opticians test children with a learning disability. This is the device referred to in the "No, No, No, I won't Go" story.

He is passionate about books and when flirting with a different career he did try and write a few himself. He had a literary agent for a while but they left soon after to become a coffee barista and he lost his contract. He hopes this wasn't because of having him as a client.

Contact Simon at:

0191 375 75 44

simon@simonberry.co.uk

Or visit his website:

www.simonberry.co.uk

About Lucy Catchpole

Lucy is a children's author, but she doesn't like to be described like that. She volunteers at her local primary school and spends time reading to, and inspiring, young children. She also writes stories for young adults.

Her imagination was ignited at an early age by her father's bedtime stories. These were anything but cosy and crammed full of adventure, intrigue, and derring-do. They often sent her diving under the bed clothes, but fortunately she came out again and started writing her own stories.

Her favourite words are blancmange, indubitably and carte blanche. She also makes words up!

Contact Lucy:

wordadventures@outlook.com

About Tim Cole

I have spent my whole life wishing I were an illustrator. Drawing from the young age of 6 in infant three all the way through my life up until I graduated from Manchester Met in the summer of 2002. Then I quickly realised the world of animation and illustration is a tough racket and those lucky enough to get paid for what they love doing aren't going anywhere!

While at Uni and pretty much working full time in my pub, I created a business drawing advertising blackboards in various clubs and bars throughout Manchester, which was at least some way to make money from it, although I have to tell you blackboard artist turf war was a real thing, just like ice-cream vans!

Following this, in an attempt to stay 'arty' I became a graphic designer, doing jobs here and there until pure nepotism and a bit of luck opened the door into the medical world. I got my first 'real' job as the medical poster maker in the Ophthalmic imaging department of Manchester

Royal Eye Hospital. This is where my career took an unexpected route into the world of Medical photography.

After learning the ins and out of photographing eyeballs I left Manchester after 6 years and took my family to my wife's hometown of Blackpool where once again fate played in my favour and gave me the chance to work as a photographer at Blackpool Victoria hospital, this time as a general medical photographer. Here I stayed for a further 3 years before the allure of the ophthalmic imaging industry drew me out of the NHS.

I now work as a trainer for a German company called Heidelberg Engineering, having worked in the industry for the past 8 years. It's a very time-consuming job which has me travelling all over the world but now, thanks to the eye world and meeting Simon Berry, I have had this incredible opportunity to get back into illustration with the Gilesgate Story Challenge!

This will be the first book I have illustrated and my first published work in many years. It has been a joy to work with Simon and read all the amazing children's stories to finally make the very difficult decision to go with The Tragic Tale of Jake the Snail. I must thank Simon for this enthusiasm and drive to keep this project moving forwards, but most of all for liking my drawings!

I truly hope you enjoy our book and most of all congratulations to Jaden for this excellent piece of writing.

Contact Tim:

Timcole1979@gmail.com

Website (or bin of images):

https://timecole.blogspot.com/

About Miles Nelson

Miles is an aspiring author from Durham. He is currently working with New Writing North training to facilitate young writers' groups, as he adores helping and inspiring young writers to hone their skills.

In his own writing, Miles specializes in sci-fi and fantasy, although he has a special soft spot for nature writing.

An interesting fact about Miles is that he enjoys collecting books about animals, from the fantastical to those we see every day.

Contact Miles:

milesnelson1997@outlook.com

Acknowledgements

This is the first ever Gilesgate Story Challenge and there are a lot of people to thank for their help in getting this book published.

Thanks to the people who donated prizes:

- Durham Wildlife Trust
- New Writing North
- Tim Cole
- Simon Berry Optometrist

Special thanks to our judges for giving their time. Especially Miles Nelson for type-setting and providing the doodles.

Thank you to Waterstones Durham and Kat for being so supportive of this project.

But most importantly, thanks to all the schools that have inspired these authors to write their stories.

St. Josephs, St. Hildes, Gilesgate Primary, Belmont Primary, Nettlesworth, Trinity and St. Anthonys.

See you all next year!